TECHNOLOGY AND KNOWLEDGE TRANSFER IN CHINA

Technology and Knowledge Transfer in China

RICHARD LI-HUA
Newcastle Business School
University of Northumbria at Newcastle, UK

ASHGATE

Published by
Ashgate Publishing Limited
Gower House
Croft Road
Aldershot
Hants GU11 3HR
England

Ashgate Publishing Company
Suite 420
101 Cherry Street
Burlington, VT 05401-4405
USA

Ashgate website: http://www.ashgate.com

British Library Cataloguing in Publication Data
Li-Hua, Richard
    Technology and knowledge transfer in China. - (The Chinese
    economy series)
    1.Technology transfer - China 2.Joint ventures - China
    3.International business enterprises - China 4.China -
    Economic conditions - 2000- 5.China - Economic policy -
    2000-
    I.Title
    338.9'26'0951

Library of Congress Cataloging-in-Publication Data
Li-Hua, Richard, 1958-
    Technology and knowledge transfer in China / Richard Li-Hua.
      p. cm. -- (The Chinese economy series)
Includes bibliographical references and index.
    ISBN 0-7546-3928-2
    1. Technology transfer--China. I. Title. II. Series.

    T174.3.L52 2004
    338.951'06--dc22
                                                        2003024000

ISBN 0 7546 3928 2

Printed in Great Britain by Antony Rowe Ltd, Chippenham, Wiltshire.

Contents

List of Figures

List of Tables

Preface

The celebration of the Chinese New Year of 2003 was filled with the amazing news that the German technology behind the magnetic train in Shanghai had reached the fastest speed (500 kilometres per hour), on the first magnetic railway in the world. It was this magnetic train service from Shanghai Pudong Longyang to Shanghai Pudong International Airport which was officially opened by the Chinese Premier, Zhu Rongji and the German Chancellor, Gerhard Schroeder on 31st December, 2002. As a result of this special event *technology transfer* again became a popular term in China. It has been recognised that technology transfer is a crucial and dynamic factor in social and economic development. Technology has been transferred intentionally or unintentionally. Sometimes, a generator of technology has acquired a competitive advantage by undertaking the dissemination of products, processes and maintenance systems. Sometimes, a recipient (or transferee) has done much better than the original innovator. For example, it was the Chinese who invented gunpowder, but the Europeans who used it and developed it further for world conquest. Sometimes the technology has taken a new form at each transfer, absorbing local traditions of design or local market preferences. However, there is value added on during each process of transfer of technology.

It is a pleasure that the publication of the current book coincides with the opening of the Shanghai magnetic train, where people not only in China but also across the globe are talking about *technology transfer*. Therefore, this publication at such a time makes sense as it not only examines aspects of technology transfer, but also addresses the appropriateness and effectiveness of technology transfer. Following the establishment of a theoretical framework for analysing the technology transfer process between construction industries in different countries, this book presents findings from an investigation of international joint venture projects in the People's Republic of China. A Structured Survey was carried out in Xinjiang, Henan and Jiangsu Provinces after a case study had been completed on a huge Sino-foreign joint venture demonstration project at Xiaolangdi in Henan Province. Both studies adopted a cross-cultural approach to its investigation. An Assessment Inventory was designed for data collection on a case study. This proved to be useful technique and was modified for the Structured Survey. The findings suggested important implications for the relationship between technology transfer and economic development. Technology and knowledge transfer is not obtainable if there is too big a gap in terms of economic development between transferor and transferee.

Moreover, knowledge transfer itself has a number of components, of which it is argued that explicit knowledge and tacit knowledge transfer are the most significant. There are a number of mechanisms already in place for explicit knowledge transfer and this study used the term *Method Statement* as a means of investigating their effectiveness. It was concluded that such systems are generally being used to good effect. Nevertheless, tacit knowledge transfer is considerably more haphazard and it is in this area that knowledge transfer can falter and technology transfer can be impeded. This study suggests means by which tacit knowledge transfer could be improved. In addition, it also leads the way for the introduction of systematic processes that could be specifically incorporated into the World Bank projects that involve international technology transfer as a major feature.

Furthermore, the study indicates that certain aspects of knowledge transfer are paralleled by the notional progression of economic development. In other words, there are features of knowledge transfer that appear to be associated with levels of economic development. To put it differently, this relationship between knowledge transfer and economic development is positively effected. This study suggests that the desire to obtain more tacit knowledge increases and the desire to obtain more explicit knowledge decreases with the levels of economic development. In other words, in a developing economy, people are more thirsty for explicit or hard knowledge, such as a specific technology to manufacture a product that enables people to survive rather than for tacit or soft knowledge, such as management know-how that enables an economy to have sustainable growth.

I sincerely hope that the readers may get answers from this book to frequent asked questions, such as what exactly is transferred, what needs to be transferred, and how and why, when talking about technology transfer and knowledge transfer.

Dr Richard Li-Hua
Newcastle upon Tyne
United Kingdom

About the Author

Richard Li-Hua is currently MBA Project Leader-China at the Newcastle Business School, University of Northumbria at Newcastle, the United Kingdom, where he teaches strategic challenge and management, knowledge management and international strategy on technology transfer. In the meantime, as Development Manager-China in the International Office of the University, he has been successfully assisting the University for the last five years in developing and implementing proactive and innovative international development strategy, including the design and delivery of multi-disciplinary consultancy and training programmes.

Richard's current research interest focuses on international strategy of technology transfer, in particular, strategic issues on knowledge transfer in Sino-foreign joint venture projects in the People's Republic of China. He is active in publishing papers and attending international academic conferences. His previous published works published by China Building Publishing House in the 1990s include *Psychology in Construction Management*, and *Contract Management for International Projects*, which were highly praised by academics and experts in the construction industry. Both of them were selected as course books in a number of universities in China.

As a senior researcher and business consultant, he has long been involved in managing corporate partnerships, strategic planning and implementation, international marketing research, business development and contract negotiation for his previous Chinese and current UK employer. He has been visiting professor at Zhengzhou University, Wuhan University, University of International Business and Economics in Beijing, China Ocean University in Tsingdao, and Henan University in Kaifeng.

Richard has a PhD in Technology Management from University of Northumbria at Newcastle, the United Kingdom. He is Chinese and is resident in the UK.

Acknowledgements

The material and data in this book was organised and collected both from the United Kingdom and the People's Republic of China. During the long process of writing the book, the author has had great encouragement and continuous support from friends, colleagues and family. First and foremost, the author wishes to express his appreciation to Dr Bob Giddings and Dr David Greenwood, who have given continuous support and guidance to the publication of this book. The author would like to record his sincere thanks to Professor Roger Flanagan, Professor Richard Neal and Professor George Stonehouse for their valuable comments to the argument and philosophy of the book.

The author would like to express his sincere thanks to Mr Han Zhonghai, Mr Friedrich Redie, and Mr Li Fuqiang, who have provided support and assistance in enabling the author to undertake the case study in Xiaolangdi. Sincerely, the author's appreciation is extended to Professor Li Qiming, Mr Ma Yuming and Mr Zhao Peng, for their support and assistance in helping the author to carry out the Structured Survey in Jiangsu Province, Henan Province and the Xinjiang Autonomous Region, the People's Republic of China. The author would also like to record his thanks to the International Co-operation Section, Ministry of Construction, P.R.C., The Foreign Affairs Department, Yellow River Water & Hydropower Development Corporation (client of Xiaolangdi Project), The Construction Management Bureau of Jiangsu Province, Henan Province and the Xinjiang Autonomous Region, P.R.C. Without their support and assistance in arranging interviews and conducting the survey, it would have been impossible to produce the book.

The author wishes to acknowledge the informal support and contribution given by members of staff in the School of Built Environment, the International Office and the Newcastle Business School of the University of Northumbria during the long process of his working on this book.

The author must acknowledge the valuable comments to the book from Professor Aimin Chen and Professor Shunfeng Song, the Series Editors for the Chinese Economy Series and the continuous support and assistance from Brendan George, Mary Savigar, Sarah Horsley and Claire Annals from Ashgate Publishing.

Finally the author would like to acknowledge the continuous support and assistance of his family during the long process of writing this book.

Chapter 1

Introduction

Background to the Study

Technology transfer is recognised as the acquisition, adaptation and use of technological knowledge by an individual, group, or society other than the one that developed the technology. The concept of technology transfer involves more than the capacity to acquire new knowledge, or produce improved production processes (Miles, 1995). It also encompasses the capacities to link engineering and managerial skills to plan, develop and implement technological capacities to shape and accomplish the strategic and operational objectives of the host organisation.

Technology transfer has been a subject of considerable interest to many groups, such as government policymakers, international funding agencies, and business executives, because of the close relationship between technology transfer and economic growth. Technology transfer has aroused the interest of academic researchers not only from the developing countries but also from developed countries as it concerns both the transferee and the transferor. Despite all this attention, however, the concept of technology transfer and mechanisms of technology transfer remains vague, controversial, and inadequately operationalised (Samli, 1985). Technology transfer is shrouded not only in controversy and emotion, but also in considerable confusion, owing to the complexity of "technology" itself and the multiplicity of channels of its "transfer". A difficulty lies in determining what to evaluate, what to transfer, how to transfer and why, since technology transfer has two main dimensions: that from the seller/transferor to the buyer/transferee, and that relating to the effective diffusion and application of the technology (Erdilek and Rapoport, 1985).

Research Problems

The literature review provides a wide and extensive understanding of international technology transfer, e.g. its definition, history, processes and channel of technology transfer, and problems of measuring technology transfer. In particular, a long involvement of technology transfer in construction is revealed by the literature review. With a few exceptions that touch international technology transfer (Abbott, 1985; Carrillo, 1993; Bon, 1997; and Ofori, 2000), little has been done in the research area of knowledge transfer, in particular, tacit knowledge transfer. However, it has been clear that the subsequent literature review (Tsang, 1995, et al.; Maitland, 1999; Holland, 1999; and Egbu, 2000, et al.) of knowledge transfer in terms of explicit knowledge and tacit knowledge has made the research aims more focused. Hence, the research problems addressed in this study are:

- *Is technology transfer appropriately and effectively channelled?*
- *What is the relationship between technology transfer and economic growth?*

Aims and Objectives of the Study

The study tended to investigate the current mechanisms of technology transfer and the aspects of technology transfer between foreign and local managers within international joint ventures in China. Its primary aim was to establish generic principles for the effectiveness and appropriateness of technology transfer. The results may ultimately assist in assessing the efficacy of technology transfer and may inform decision-makers in the recipient and donor organisations as well as investors such as the World Bank, who impose contractual provisions that require technology transfer.

In particular the objectives of the current research project are:

- From the literature, to establish a theoretical framework for the tracking of the technology transfer process;
- To demonstrate the basic patterns of knowledge transfer through a Case Study;
- To evaluate the appropriateness and effectiveness of the study by using a Structured Survey;
- To identify the implications of the relationship between technology transfer and economic development levels.

An Overview of China's Economy

However, it would be necessary and constructive to have an overview of China's economic reforms as background information since the current study has been undertaken in the context of the construction industry in China.

The Chinese economy presents a mixture of features of a market economy intertwined with those of a command economy. It was defined, by the Chinese government, as "socialist market economy with Chinese characteristics". Since the founding of New China, especially in the last twenty years after the start of reform and the opening to the outside world in 1978, China has made great strides in economic construction and social development. However, it should be mentioned that a number of key policies made these achievements possible. The household responsibility system and partial liberalisation of agricultural prices raised agricultural production and rural incomes, especially in the early years of reform. Liberal policies toward non-state enterprises and a gradual introduction of market forces into the state-owned enterprise sector provided a powerful catalyst for rapid growth in industrial output, exports and employment (Stern, 2001).

Despite China's achievements since 1978, the Government faces significant challenges over the medium term, which can be broadly divided into two sets: achieving sustainable growth within a stable macroeconomic environment, and reducing poverty and maintaining a relatively egalitarian distribution of income and wealth.

Twenty Years of Economic Reform

During the last twenty years, China has seen the most remarkable period of economic growth in modern times. As Stern (2001) pointed out at Tsinghua University, Beijing[1]:

> China's development in this period has been characterised by a sequence of radical changes, although it has been evolutionary in the sense of building on what went before. Where the territory was uncharted, the government recognised that it was unknown and approached reforms with a pragmatic learn-as-you-go spirit. It did not matter whether the cats were black or white as long as they could catch the mice - and some experience was needed to see which cats could actually catch the mice.

Stern described the features of Chinese market economy as decentralisation, rural reforms, and experimentation and innovation with new enterprises. Each element is crucial to an understanding of how China was able to use its social and organisational capital to transform the economy and generate growth. The analysis of decentralisation, the rural economy, and new enterprises provides a context and rational for China's successful evolutionary approach to the transition, which may be summarised in a stylised way in terms of four principles or observations:

- Step-by-step progress: The Chinese experience is that an adaptive process of transition, proceeding step by step, can retain the social and organisational capital developed in previous stages of development and transform it in ways that enhance efficiency and productivity.
- Build the road as one travels: It has to be pointed out that there were strong arguments in favour of following such an evolutionary approach. It could be identified as an emergent approach to some extent.
- Climb the mountain by a zigzag path: There is no doubt that the reform path might be more zigzag than linear.
- Robust solutions: The solutions to problems, as they arise, need not be perfect. The key is to look for robust solutions, that is, resilient solutions that work reasonably well across, or can be adapted to, a range of circumstances.

---

[1] Nicholas Stern is a Senior Vice-President and Chief Economist at the World Bank. Twenty Years of Reform: Achievements, Challenges and the Challenges and New Agenda is a speech delivered by him in June, 2001 at Tsinghua University, Beijing.

However, with China joining the World Trade Organisation (WTO), there will be great opportunities and challenges as well, which have been categorised by Stern (2001) as follows:

- Enterprises, competition and the investment climate;
- Infrastructure and regulation;
- WTO accession and trade;
- Social protection and pension reform.

With each of these categories, there are institutional possibilities. However, China as in the past will choose its own approach and innovate along the way.

The World Bank's Forecast about China

The World Bank (1999) reports that China could meet the new challenges and sustain rapid growth, mainly because of its strengths: relative stability, a remarkably high savings rate, a strong record of pragmatic reforms, a disciplined and literate labour force, and growing administrative capacity. These strengths have driven the country's growth for the past two decades and will continue to do so. China's continued transformation into a larger, more open economy is likely to have far reaching consequences for other countries. Similarly, as China makes the transition into the world economy, it becomes increasingly exposed to external influences. In a recent interview with Xinhua, Uri Dadush, World Bank International Trade Director, confirmed that China can be a big voice for developing countries, that it should be heard and that China is important in all issues in WTO negotiations including those about agriculture and service. As to the improvement China has achieved over the past year since China's entry into the WTO, China is making very successful adjustments to meet WTO commitments and has made transfer an important part of its domestic reform.

The World Bank has made the long-term projection that based on current trends China's GDP measures on a purchasing parity basis, would become one of the world's largest early in the next century. This forecast assumes that a number of assumptions are fulfilled (Flanagan and Li, 1997):

- The continuation of the reform process;
- A growing ability of the authorities to control macroeconomics developments;
- The ability of relatively underdeveloped infrastructure system support growth;
- A relatively stable political environment.

From Technology Transfer to Knowledge Transfer

Research into technology transfer has matured from the early period of emphasis on the technology itself in the early period of the current study, through general management objectives to the current state of development, where interest has arisen in the appropriateness and effectiveness of international technology transfer. It has been identified during the study that without knowledge transfer, technology transfer does not take place as knowledge is the key to control technology as a whole. Knowledge transfer is essential and crucial in the process of technology transfer. Therefore, the focus of the research has been shifted from technology transfer to knowledge transfer. And attention has been drawn to the identification of not only the features of technology transfer but also that of knowledge transfer. Through the identification of the research problems concerning international technology transfer till the responses and resolution of the research problems knowledge transfer, the loop of technology transfer has been completed.

The sequence of the research project is presented in Figure 1.1 as follows:

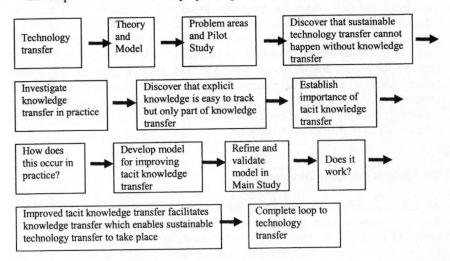

Figure 1.1 Sequence of the Research Project

How was the Study Conducted?

The research project aims to investigate aspects of technology transfer and to track the process of knowledge transfer between foreign and local managers within joint venture projects in China when they deal with Method Statement in construction. The nature of the research has decided that the design concept of the research project has been a combination of both a qualitative approach and a quantitative approach. Following the literature review, both a Case Study and a Structured Survey were designed to be an integral part of the research project. Interviews were undertaken during the Case Study in a major joint venture project in China in order to obtain qualitative data while a Structured Survey was arranged in three sampling regions in a much wider context in China.

A psychological instrument - an Assessment Inventory was used both in the Case Study and the Structured Survey. It should be pointed out that significant qualitative data was collected through the interviewing of 25 foreign and local managers in the Case Study while quantitative data were obtained by analysing 450 copies of Assessment Inventories, which were returned to the researcher.

What is the Intent of this Book?

First and foremost, this book is a highly practical, technically limited, presentation of the principles of technology transfer - a blend of technology management, knowledge management and management of international joint ventures. Furthermore, the distinctiveness of the book lies in that the understanding of tacit knowledge transfer, which has been developed and evaluated within the three different economies, will enable the recipients and donor organisations as well as international funding agencies to identify the essential ingredients of a particular aspect of technology transfer, namely the transfer of tacit knowledge. It is believed that the theoretical framework of the book may provide guidance and enable policy-makers within the governments, sponsors of projects and executives of the companies involved to address the existing deficiencies in the process of technology transfer, and assist in the development of more appropriate arrangement for the transfer of management knowledge.

To Whom is this Book Directed?

As addressed previously, this book has arguably a very wide range of readers. Researchers and academics may find the book interesting and useful because the study has employed the psychological instrument, the Assessment Inventory, used by the psychologist to assess/measure normal traits of people, such as interests, values and attitudes of human beings. The employment of the Assessment Inventory approach based on a psychological paradigm is a trial run in the construction management research in a way in which it might be regarded as an extensive justification of the traditional research approach-questionnaire approach, which has been widely and repeatedly used by researchers.

Besides senior students and academics in the areas of construction management and economics, business administration and international management, both the transferors/sellers (from the Western advanced countries in principle) and the transferees/recipients (from the developing countries in principle) are interested in the book, as it touches a subject of considerable interest to many groups, such as government policymakers, international funding agencies, and business executives. This book not only suits the business executives in the joint venture companies in construction related disciplines but also for managers at different levels in joint ventures companies as it offers golden rules for successful operation of joint ventures in China.

How is the Text Unique?

There is little literature that touches the measurement of knowledge transfer. In fact it is hard to track the process of knowledge transfer, particularly the transfer of tacit knowledge in construction, because of the nature of tacit knowledge and the sophistication and the size of the construction industry. However, this study has considered that the most feasible way would be an attempt to focus on a particular construction task so that the research problem may be approached. It is believed that it is a breakthrough to focus on tracking of the process of knowledge transfer when both foreign and local partners are dealing with Method Statement during the implementation of a project. What is important is that the process of knowledge transfer in dealing with Method Statement will mirror the process of problem-solving and decision-making as well as the process of knowledge transfer in the whole industry. Furthermore, the core competence of the book lies in presenting the data collected from three different economies and the analyses of the data, which has identified that without knowledge transfer, technology transfer does not take place as knowledge is the key to control technology as a whole. Hence, knowledge transfer is crucial in the process of technology transfer.

Outline of the Study

As has been pointed out in the section of aims and objectives, the study focused on the investigation of the current mechanisms of technology transfer and the aspects of technology transfer between foreign and local partners within international joint ventures in China. Based upon that premise, the study aimed to establish a general principle for the appropriateness and effectiveness of technology transfer. Following the theme, the theoretical framework for the current research has been built through the literature review of knowledge transfer. It should be pointed out that it might be easy to define the process of explicit knowledge while it is hard to track tacit knowledge transfer. Qualitative data were collected during the pilot study through interviews. The theoretic research model that was built during the pilot study was further refined and validated during the main study.

As the book title implies, the subject matter encompasses the following fields:

- Strategic issues of technology transfer;
- Strategic issues on knowledge transfer;
- Communication and human interaction;
- Knowledge management issues in construction industry;
- International joint venture projects;
- Construction industry in China.

Therefore, to resolve the expanse of material content, logic and sequence, the outline and design concept of the study has to be closely related with the above focuses. Each chapter begins with a brief introduction, then examines problems and issues, and ends with a discussion.

Chapter 1 looks at the research problem and issues of technology transfer, the aims and objectives of the current research project, an overview of China's economy, with particular examination of how the research focus was shifted from technology transfer to knowledge transfer. Chapter 2 examines the definition, history, channels, theory and practice of technology transfer, the policies of EC and the World Bank towards technology transfer, and the measurement and appropriateness of technology transfer. Chapter 3 reviews the definition and the important role of construction, the construction industry in China, aspects of internationalisation of the construction industry in China, and issues and options of technology transfer in construction. Chapter 4 examines theories of communication and aspects of knowledge transfer, distinction of explicit knowledge and tacit knowledge, problems and practicalities in knowledge transfer, and knowledge management programme in construction. Chapter 5 looks at methodological issues that relate to the current research. It examines the concept of research design and philosophical notions of the study. It explains the methods used both in the pilot study and the main study. Chapter 6 examines the various issues of the pilot study, the international joint venture projects in China. The analysis and findings of pilot study data is presented. Chapter 7 examines a comprehensive comparative study of economic indicators of Jiangsu Province, Henan Province and Xinjiang Autonomous Region, P.R.C.. The different positions of the three economies have been identified. Chapter 8 examines the aspects of the main study that was undertaken in Jiangsu Province, Henan Province and Xinjiang Autonomous Region, P.R.C.. The analysis and discussion of the main study data are presented. Chapter 9 examines correlation and implication between knowledge transfer and economic development by incorporating a Pearson Correlation analysis method. The relationship between knowledge transfer and economic development was further explored and discussed based upon the previous chapter. Chapter 10 re-examines the aims and objectives of the study and looks at the research findings, validation of the research model, policy implication, and contribution to knowledge. Further research is recommended.

Scope and Key Assumptions

The current study sets its boundaries within the context of the construction industry in China. Therefore, the pilot study and the main study of the present research project were designed and arranged in China. In particular, the main study was undertaken in three different regions in terms of economic development in China while the pilot study was carried out in a major international joint venture project in China. The unit of analysis of the study was various 'dyads' or management pairs with one foreign element and one local element, and whose roles demanded that they work together (refer to Figure 6.3.). From an academic point of view, the study should generate profound data and useful information. Of the many research works concerned with technology transfer, relatively few have tried to approach the tracking of knowledge transfer process, which is the core issue of technology transfer. At present there has not been much research in the area of knowledge transfer, in particular, the transfer of tacit knowledge. However, it is believed that the current research work has provided a systematic and theoretical guiding principle that has not existed hitherto in an area that has attracted little previous research.

The distinctiveness of the research programme lies in developing and validating a general principle with which the recipients and donor organisations as well as international funding agencies can identify the essential ingredients of a particular aspect of technology transfer, namely the transfer of tacit knowledge. This may enable the practitioners to address the existing deficiencies in the process of technology transfer and assist in the development of more appropriate arrangement for the transfer of management know-how in theory and in practice.

Summary

This chapter has outlined the structure of the book and laid the foundations for the whole book. It has introduced an overview of China's economy. It presented the research problem and the justification of the research. It explained the key issues of the current research project, from technology transfer to knowledge transfer. Furthermore, the research methodology was briefly described and justified. The philosophical notion of the book was outlined and the limitations were given. On these foundations, the book can proceed with a detailed description of the research project.

Chapter 2

Philosophical Notions and Structure of the Book

Introduction

The primary interest of the study is to identify how management know-how is transferred between foreign and local managers within international joint ventures in China. It is believed that the identification of this transfer process involves cross-cultural research. In order to have an extensive understanding of the foreign and local elements, therefore, the aspects of cross-cultural research have been examined with a review of creative problem-solving in the real life world. However, it is important to have a process observation of knowledge transfer between foreign and local managers. It should be noted that these premises have directly contributed to the design of the study.

Furthermore, two concepts, internal and external validity, are fundamental and crucial to developing research designs (Vaus, 2001). Ideally research design should be both internally and externally valid. Therefore, the research project is composed of two major studies – the Case Study and the Structured Survey, both of which are designed to be an integral part of the study. It has been recognised that the Case Study will certainly generate valuable results, which might be the causal conclusions. However, it is believed that the Structured Survey will generate result in a much wider context, which will sustain the external validity.

The measurement of the process of knowledge transfer between foreign and local managers involves the observation of human interaction, measurement of attitude and interests as well as motivation. Therefore, psychological instruments and methodology have been approached, as psychology is defined as the scientific study of the human behaviour and the process of human thinking. Furthermore, based on a series of inventories (Melvin, 1979; Lee, 1990; Gatchel and Mears, 1982; Cohen, Swerdlik and Phillips, 1996) that measure intelligence, personality, interest, preference and decision-making, the thought of designing an Assessment Inventory for the current study has formed into shape. Therefore, a psychological instrument-Assessment Inventory has been designed and introduced into the study.

Design Concepts of the Study

According to Tashakkori (1998), there are two schools in the field of social and behavioural science, which are represented by a positivist/empiricist and a constructivist/phenomenological orientation. The positivist paradigm underlines what is called quantitative methods for explanatory research while the constructivist paradigm emphasises qualitative methods for exploratory research.

It has been recognised that academic debates raged in the social and behavioural sciences regarding the superiority of one or the other of the two major social sciences paradigms or models between positivist and constructivist. However, in most cases, the researchers incline to the view point of pacifists, who appear to present the compatibility thesis based on a different paradigm, which has been referred to as pragmatism. In order to minimise discrepancies between the data collected during the study and the phenomenon of the real world, the current research project has adopted a mixed methodology that combines both qualitative and quantitative approaches. As the research topic implies, the current research project is deemed to be cross-cultural research which involves unearthing the process of creative problem solving in the real world with particular reference to tracking the transfer process of tacit knowledge between foreign and local managers. Therefore, an extensive understanding and clarification of the basic elements and the implications of the following issues are essential and crucial.

Cross-Cultural Research

Cross-cultural research has both theoretical and practical advantages. Goodwin (1996) crystallises the complexities and the significance of cross-cultural research. He points out:

> [...] more recent concerns (about methodology and ethics, generalisability and relevance of much psychological work) have stimulated a resurgence of interest in the universality of psychological theories and consequently in cross-cultural variation in both the content and the processes of human interaction.

Cross-cultural research is important because it can serve a number of purposes. After examining the current literatures, Goodwin (1996) summarises four points:

- It can help address important issues concerning the way in which individual personality factors interact with wider societal forces;
- It can be used to test apparently 'universal' and competing theories under particularly stringent conditions – i.e. those where there is considerable cultural variation;
- It allows people to learn directly from other cultures, particularly where these are undesirable social activities (such as relationship violence);

- The acculturation processes in new or changing societies have important implications for a range of social behaviour.

Process Observation and Process Measurement

Holt (1997) explains that:

> Any hypothesised alternative or improvement to existing practice or knowledge, cannot be properly considered, until the existing conditions and problems surrounding it, are fully understood. Much of this understanding will emanate from the literature search, but this in isolation will rarely suffice. A first and most simple complement to the literature search is observation. Observation alone may be considered as a qualitative methodology, yielding some understanding of the way a process or condition is conducted, or exist at present. In this context, process observation is most often recorded as a narrative (vis-a-vis numeric data).

Holt (1997) further points out:

> [...] process measurement in this context could involve time study; this being the recording of times taken to perform a task, so that an output standard may be established.[...], many aspects of built environment research utilise questionnaire surveys. The most straightforward of these is the open question survey, which employs a questionnaire inviting any written reply to the question set.

The primary interest of the current research is to investigate the current mechanisms of technology transfer and the aspects of technology transfer between foreign and local partners within international joint ventures in China. Furthermore, the research aims to investigate in particular the process of knowledge transfer. Therefore, much enlightenment of the philosophical thought in the design of research methodology of the current research has been drawn from the above literature. With consideration of the paradigms and politics of the current research project, Process Observation and Process Measurement have been regarded as critical issues during the whole process of the research.

Structure of the Current Research Project

Given the design concept of the research, the structure of the current research has come into shape. *Firstly*, a literature review of the current state of technology transfer has developed the theoretical framework for the study. Moreover, a review of the literature in knowledge management and knowledge transfer has provided a further and extensive understanding of the research problems and contemporary phenomenon of knowledge transfer, in particular, the mechanisms and process of both explicit and tacit knowledge transfer. *Secondly*, the Case Study has bridged the theoretical review of literature in the academic world and the practical approach of the knowledge transfer phenomenon at the real construction site, which has built a platform for the in-depth understanding of research problems and undertaking the Structured Survey. *And thirdly*, by using an Assessment Inventory, data have been collected and a theoretical framework has been constructed in the studies. Table 2.1 represents the structure of the current research project.

Table 2.1 Structure of the current research project

Phase	Programmes	Academic Activities	Methodology Employed
Phase One	Literature Review	Current state of knowledge Technology Transfer Internationalisation Construction industry in China Knowledge management Knowledge transfer Explicit knowledge Tacit knowledge	Research notes Keeping diaries Reading Writing
Phase Two	Case Study	Case Study in Xiaolangdi 6 study trips to Xiaolangdi Project 1 knowledge transfer seminar 25 interviewees 52 copies of assessment inventories Demonstration and presentation Analysis and discussion Feedback and modification Validation Contribution to knowledge	Survey Interview Semi-structured interview Structured interview Assessment Inventory
Phase Three	Structured Survey	Structured Survey in Jiangsu, Henan and Xinjiang, P.R.C. Visit of construction authorities of Henan and Jiangsu, P.R.C. 450 copies of assessment inventories from Henan, Jiangsu and Xinjiang, P.R.C. Demonstration and presentation Analysis and discussion Feedback and modification Validation Contribution to knowledge	Structured Survey Assessment Inventory

Assessment Inventory

Melvin (1979) defines psychology as the study of the human behaviour. He points out that:

> It investigates behaviour, stripping away the veneer of myth and irrational beliefs, so that one may more realistically comprehend why people act in certain ways. [...], Granted that psychology lacks the precision of physics, but it certainly exceeds the accuracy and perception of a rigid personality cemented together with prejudgement and prejudice.

Psychologists, aided by concepts of applied statistics, in addressing human relations in construction management, are much more restrictive and precise in their terminology and measurements (Melvin, 1979). In the field of psychology, researchers used personality inventories to assess/measure normal traits of people, such as sociability, emotional stability, the need to achieve, and a number of others. The notable personality inventories to measure interests, values and attitudes of human being are:

- The Strong-Compbell Interest Inventory.
- The Kuder Preference Record-Vocational.
- The Harrington/O'Shea System for Career Decision-Making.

In addition to the terminology and measurement addressed by psychologists, Whyte (1997) points out that for studies of attitudes and interest of people in an organisation or community, the questionnaire survey along with interview is the appropriate instrument. For the field interview, the researchers are only interested in how the person's experience led him or her to form the attitudes in question. In consideration of the validity and reliability of the methodology used, it has to be pointed out that the questionnaire survey has been modified into a Structured Survey with Assessment Inventory. Much of the design concept of Assessment Inventory for the current research project has been derived from the personality inventories that were designed by psychologists. The employment of the assessment inventories approach based on psychological paradigm is a trial run in the construction management research in a way in which it might be regarded as an extensive justification to the traditional research approach-questionnaire approach, which has been widely and repeatedly used by researchers.

Structured Survey

When a psychologist wishes to assess causes of behaviour without waiting for a result to occur naturally, or when the behaviour essentially precludes observation, he may elect for the Structured Survey method (Melvin, 1979). In doing so, the underlying reasons for the behaviour might be directly inquired by asking questions. Therefore, considerable data can be accumulated in a relatively short time. Furthermore, surveys, which are under controlled and systematic circumstances, will provide surprisingly informative results (i.e. public opinions, election predications, consumer surveys). In fact, politicians and union officials often determine policies based on survey findings. Two major deficiencies may possibly occur in the survey method: (1) the subjects may willingly or unconsciously distort the true causes of their behaviour; and (2) a biased sample may result in an erroneous picture of the population segment that the investigator desires to study. Therefore, for keeping the data as accurate as possible, a Structured Survey was carried out among the construction authorities and construction managers by delivering assessment inventories personally by the researcher during the main study.

Correlation of Responses with Levels of Economic Development

In the current study, the data from three different provinces in China were examined to see whether there is any association between the data gathered and the level of economic development of each province. The correlation technique employed is Pearson's Product-Moment Correlation Coefficient (Pearson's *r*). Karl Pearson was a pioneer of regression techniques and his *product-moment correlation coefficient* is today the most commonly used correlation technique.

Pearson's *r* is properly applied to data that are numerically discrete or continuous. By contrast, categorical data require other correlation techniques such as the *contingency coefficient*, and ranking scale data may be analysed using the *rank-order correlation* methods. Correlation concerns the relationship between variables; a correlation coefficient is a statistic used to express quantitatively the extent to which two variables are related (Lee, 1999). Examples of the use of Pearson's *r* are commonly found in the Construction Management literature. Examples include exploration of the correlation between the comprising resolution styles and the satisfaction levels of contractors (Yu and Leung, 2001), and the correlation between the value of Australia building completed and K value and B value (Mak, Ng, Chen and Varnam, 2000).

Method Statement in the Studies

In the construction industry, it has long been a common belief that the planning of construction methods is a subject that cannot be taught but rather only learned by experience. Such a situation was undoubtedly true when the importance of detailed planning of construction methods was recognised in the 1950s. However, the Method Statement is one of the most important documents in the planning process. Based on the Method Statement, the job was priced, the cost breakdown of the tender sum was done, and specialist staff for the supervision of subcontractors were arranged. The availability of work study facilities to evaluate performance and provide recommendations for improvements in efficiency, and the use of program systems appropriate to the contract in question (Illingworth, 1998). Such systems will need to allow rapid assimilation of progress situations and provide weekly or short-term methods of giving easily understood communication to first line supervision.

There is little literature that touches the measurement of knowledge transfer. In fact it is hard to track the process of knowledge transfer, particularly the transfer of tacit knowledge in construction, because of the nature of tacit knowledge and the sophistication and the large dimension of the construction industry. It has been considered that the feasible way would be an attempt in focusing on a particular construction task so that the research problem may be approached. It is believed that it is a breakthrough to focus on tracking the process of knowledge transfer when both foreign and local partners are dealing with the Method Statement during the implementation of a project. What is important is that the process of knowledge transfer in dealing with the Method Statement will mirror the process of problem-solving and decision-making as well as the process of knowledge transfer in the whole industry.

Summary

This chapter explicates the design concepts and the philosophical notion of the practice of the current study, and of the methodologies to be employed both in the Case Study and the Structured Survey. It has to be pointed out that whatever methodologies employed in the study has to demonstrate the potential to solve the research problems.

The special nature of the current research requires the identification of the knowledge transfer process between foreign and local elements, which is cross-cultural research.

Both explicit knowledge and tacit knowledge have their own way of being transferred. In most of the cases, the transfer of tacit knowledge involves the process of creative problem-solving in the real life world. This research project involves a large amount of field-work on the construction site.

Chapter 3

Development and Current State of Understanding of Technology Transfer

Introduction

Technology transfer has been a focus of considerable research interest because of its close relationship with economic growth. It has been assuming an increasing significance for both developed and developing countries. In this chapter an attempt is made to establish a clear picture of the definition, theory, channels, measurement issues, and appropriateness of international technology transfer. Based upon the above elements, the study will concentrate on the identification of mechanisms of technology transfer and the processes of technology transfer. Furthermore, the chapter reviews the approaches and issues in measuring technology transfer.

What is Technology?

Technology represents the combination of human understanding of natural laws and phenomena accumulated since ancient times to make things that fulfil our needs and desires or that perform certain functions (Karatsu, 1990). In other words, technology has to create things that benefit human beings. Miles (1995) defines technology as the means by which we apply our understanding of the natural world to the solution of practical problems. It is the practical application of scientific or engineering knowledge to the co-operation, development or application of products or offering processes or operations. It is a combination of "hardware" (buildings, plant and equipment) and "software" (skills, knowledge, experience together with suitable organisational and institutional arrangement).

The UN Conference on Trade and Development (UNCTAD) has provided the following definition:

> Technology is bought and sold as capital goods including machinery and productive systems, human labour usually skilled manpower, management and specialised scientists. Information of both technical and commercial character, including that which is readily available, and that subject to proprietary rights and restrictions.

Technology cannot merely be considered as a production factor, and it is not socially neutral (Mnaas, 1990). It seems much easier for understanding "technology" to consider the concept of "technology" as consisting of four closely inter-linked elements: namely, technique, knowledge (normally being considered as "technology"), the organisation of the production and the product. However, knowledge does not make sense if the organisation of the relevant production goes without producing meaningful products. Therefore, technology must be applied and maintained, which implies a demand for a further input of a suitable range of human resources and skills. However, it should be noticed that it is this latter input that is at the root of the difficulty in transferring technologies between different environments.

Technique

Technique covers the instruments of labour (machinery and tools), materials and the way they are brought into function by labour in the working process. Both social dynamic (working process) and social contradictions (e.g. between machinery and labour) are inherent in this element of the technology as in each of the sub-concepts.

Knowledge

Knowledge consists of three principal categories: applied science, skills, and intuition. The weighting between these categories of knowledge is changing historically, but in every case an adequate combination of types of knowledge must be present. *Knowledge is the 'key to control' over technology as a whole*, which can be seen both at micro-level (Taylorism) and at higher levels of social aggregation (technological dependency) (Mnaas, 1990). However, it is helpful for understanding that knowledge has recently been classified as explicit knowledge and tacit knowledge.

Organisation

Technique and knowledge must be organised before they can bring results. Organisation is therefore an integral part of technology. Organisation of a working process of technique and knowledge into a product may have technical causes, but mostly the actual choice of organisation will rest widely on social-economic causes and reflect the general social structure of society.

Product

The ultimate purpose of bringing technique, knowledge and organisation together is of course to obtain a product. Without including this goal, it is in fact difficult to understand the other three elements properly. It seems natural to include the product in a comprehensive technology concept, not least because in practice, the choice of product often precedes the choice of the technique, knowledge and organisation by which it is going to be produced.

Rosenberg and Frischtak (1985) pointed out that the specificity of technology has close links with the nature of the inputs to its production and of the resulting outputs. In most advanced countries, at least 60 percent of research and development expenditure is on development, namely expenditure to develop specific products or production processes. Figure 3.1 represents the distribution of the costs of innovation (excluding normal investment in plant and equipment in industrial firms). Depending on the assumptions made, this distribution of expenditures predicts that between 10 and 30 percent of the inputs to industrial technology come from outside industry (mainly universities and government laboratories), and the remainder from within industry itself.

Technology Transfer

Technology transfer is a crucial and dynamic factor in social and economic development. Technology has been transferred intentionally or unintentionally.

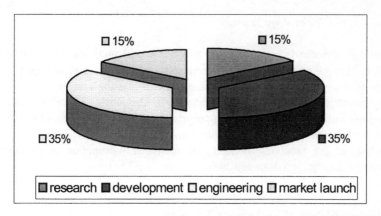

Figure 3.1 Distribution of the cost of innovation (Rosenberg and Frischtak, 1985)

Sometimes, a generator of technology has acquired a competitive advantage by undertaking the dissemination of products, processes and maintenance systems (Bradbury, 1978). Sometimes, a recipient (or transferee) has done much better than the original innovator. For example, historically the Chinese invented gunpowder, however the Europeans who used it and developed it further for their purpose. Sometimes the technology has taken a new form at each transfer, absorbing local traditions of design or local market preferences. However, there is value added on during each process of transfer.

Definition of Technology Transfer

The two words "technology transfer" seem to convey different meanings to different people and different organisations. Technology transfer is defined in the Work Regulations of the United Nations, as the "transfer of systematic knowledge for the manufacture of a product or provision of service" (Yu, 1991). It has been defined in many other ways. According to Abbott, (1985), it is the movement of science and technology from one group to another, such movement involving their use. Traditionally, technology transfer was conceptualised as the transfer of hardware objects, but today it also often involves information (e.g. a computer software programme or a new idea) that may be completely devoid of any hardware aspects.

The concept of technology transfer is comprehensive, including commercial transactions and non-commercial technical aid. If this transfer involves any factors that are beyond domestic control, the transfer takes on an international aspect, therefore, that comes under the umbrella of international technology transfer, the content of which covers license agreement, technical services, technical consulting, etc. International technology transfer includes co-operation production, joint-venture operation, operation of project in co-operation, and project-contracting (Yu, 1991).

Significance of Technology Transfer

Technology transfer is important not only for world understanding, but also for taking advantage of progress in different parts of the world in applying modern science to economic activity. At the same time, it is a shortcut not only for Third World countries, but also for all countries in the world. However, success in technology transfer is related to its appropriateness and effectiveness (Samli, 1985). If the transferred technology is not appropriate for the needs and conditions prevailing in the receiving country, no matter how superior or efficient that technology may be, it will be rejected.

The Recent History of Technology Transfer

In its broadest sense, technology transfer has occurred since the very earliest stages of the human development, and social and economic development. Having defined and identified the significance of technology transfer, this section examines the recent history of technology transfer from the 1960s to the 1990s. Knowledge management emerged as a focus of business attention in late 1995[1] and began to

---

[1] Examples include: *The Journal of Knowledge Management, Knowledge Management, Knowledge Management Magazine, Knowledge Management Review,* etc.

prevail as technology transfer began to fade in the 1990s. Knowledge management and knowledge transfer were popular until recently.

UN Conference on Science and Technology

The interest in technology transfer on a global scale can be traced to the early 1960s. The concept of "technology transfer" was debated during the UN Conference on Science and Technology (UNCSAT) which was held in Geneva in 1963. The advanced countries prepared their scientific and technological wares and the developing nations were expected to pick and choose those aspects that might help solve their development problems. One distinguished British Nobel Laureate referred to the UNCSAT as "a supermarket" (Oldham, 1987). The difficulties of access to technology and the costs of technology were not seriously considered. In fact the real problems of technology transfer were hardly discussed at all.

The Organisation of American States

According to Oldham (1987), the Organisation of American States was the earliest organization to recognise the developmental importance of technology transfer and initiated their studies in Latin America. They built on work by Constantine Vaitsos that had already begun in Colombia and set up a network of studies in most Latin American countries.

UN Conference on Trade and Development

UN Conference on Trade and Development (UNCTAD) is one of the first international organisations to recognise that there were problems associated with the transfer of technology to developing countries. In its second conference in New Delhi in 1968, UNCTAD commissioned a paper that used Organisation for Economic Co-operation and Development statistics to compare the technological balance of payments between different countries. Some industrialised countries sold more than they purchased and their balance of payments was positive, whereas developing countries had the reverse. Therefore, UNCTAD argued that this "invisible" trade in technology warranted further study and began a major programme to identify the main policy issues about technology transfer, which they feel, should be of concern to Third World governments.

Technology Transfer in the 1970s

The result of the study of technology transfer in Latin America caught the attention of the developing world. With technology transfer, the multinational companies appeared to be making excessive profits out of their sales to Latin America. Technology transfer aroused increasing interest of academics. At the same time the issue of technology transfer had become so politically charged that it featured on the agenda of a meeting of Latin American foreign ministers.

Throughout the 1970s, technology transfer remained a major political issue (Oldham, 1987). For 10 years UNCTAD tried to negotiate a Code of Conduct on Technology Transfer which would be binding on both suppliers and recipients of technology. The debate between government representatives in Geneva's UNCTAD headquarters became extremely acrimonious, and much time and money was spent on negotiations that were eventually fruitless. There were arguments over excessive profits and the price charged for technology transfer between the developed and the developing countries.

At the same time many developing countries set up government mechanisms to monitor and control the flow of foreign technology. These countries followed what came to be called 'defensive' technology transfer policies. They aimed at improving the contractual terms of those that were permitted entry into the country.

Technology Transfer in the 1980s and 1990s - Fear of Competition

The prominent features of the interrelated developments of international technology transfer in the1980s are summarised by Singer (1991) as follows:

- Internationalisation of production;
- Globalisation of competition;
- The proliferation of new information technologies and several types of organisational innovations relating to design, production and marketing of industrial goods and services.

In the 1980s, the concerns about contractual conditions and terms began to fade as a new set of issues began to arise. This was mainly caused by the success of such countries as Brazil and South Korea in competing with their manufactured goods in international markets. This led companies in the developed world to be even more reluctant to part with their "core" or essential technologies at whatever price.

Technology Transfer and EC Policies During the 1980s and the early 1990s, European Commission policies and programs on technology transfer opened new ways of thinking about innovation support systems and shaped a number of infrastructures and services for such purpose. The most important have been contributions from the Strategic Program for Innovation and Technology Transfer (SPRINT), the Regional Innovation and Technology Transfer Strategies and Infrastructures (RITTS), the pilot-action of Regional Technology Plans (TRP), and recently, the Fifth Community Frame-work Program for Research and Technological Development. These programs have accumulated important experiences in technological co-operation and created generic tools for technology transfer and innovation diffusion (Komninos, 1997).

The World Bank and Technology Transfer The World Bank is one of the organisations that are most interested in technology transfer. It supports the view that the development of local consulting firms can best be advanced through ventures with foreign firms. In 1993, however, the World Bank adopted an explicit policy of requiring a commitment to technology transfer from its contractors to the construction industries of the host country (Abbott, 1986).

The World Bank has an explicit policy of promoting technology transfer by using international consulting firms to support and strengthen local capacities. The World Bank is always keen to promote technology transfer and frequently advises that foreign companies will not get Bank project contracts unless they form meaningful partnerships with local companies (Carrillo, 1993). However, there is a lack of mechanisms to ensure real technology transfer. In her study of international joint ventures, Carrillo's findings show that international joint-venture between contractors in the developed and developing countries are recognised as a potential means of enhancing the construction expertise of nationals of developing countries, and offer many advantages and disadvantages to its partners.

Technology Transfer: Issues and Practice

It is clear that technology can no longer be regarded as information that is generally applicable and easy to reproduce and re-use but as a highly differentiated range of techniques (Tsang, 1997). Neither can technical knowledge only be interpreted in terms of production technology, as Kogut and Zander (1992) point out. People and organisations possess socially oriented as well as technologically oriented know-how (Menzler-Hokkanen, 1995) and a firm's technologies are embodied in its human and organisational as well as its physical resources. Successful transfer of hard technologies often has to be accompanied by the transfer of soft technologies like management know-how (Hendryx, 1986). These are particularly critical since they are sensitive to local cultural and environmental conditions (Bakuli, 1994).

This section reviews a range of issues and practices of technology transfer, which covers technology transfer process, channels and relevant issues of evaluation of technology transfer.

Technology Transfer Process

Technology may be transferred between persons, between organisations, from a research centre or educational institution to enterprises in industries and between regions and countries. In its most common usage, technology transfer normally refers to formal and direct arrangements based on an agreement between a buyer and a seller or a non-commercial arrangement between a donor and a beneficiary. However, a funding agency can play an important role in the arrangement. Ofori

(1994) illustrates the process of technology transfer between countries as shown in Figure 3.2.

Technology Transfer Channels

As identified by Sharif (1983) the complexity of technology and transfer process, motivations and the practices of the transferors, attitudes and the abilities of the transferees and the government policies are the major issues of technology transfer. Reddy (1996) identifies six barriers to technology transfer: political, regional, social, religious, ethical, and economic. After a survey of the literature of technology transfer, Rapoport (1985) summarised the channels of technology transfer as follows:

- Direct foreign investment.
- Sale of turnkey plants.
- Joint venture.
- Co-operative research arrangement.
- Export of high technology products and capital goods.
- Reverse engineering.
- Exchange of scientific and technical personnel.
- Science and technology conference.
- Trade shows and exhibits.
- Education and training of foreigners.
- Commercial visits.
- Open literature (journals, magazines, technical books and articles).
- Industrial espionage.
- End-user or third country diversions.
- And government assistance programmes.

The technology lag in the construction industries of the developing countries makes technology transfer more necessary and potentially viable (Abbott, UNCTC, 1989). Therefore, developing countries should promote international strategic alliances, such as joint ventures between local and multi-national contractors in order to enhance their management capacity and develop their construction industries (World Bank, 1984).

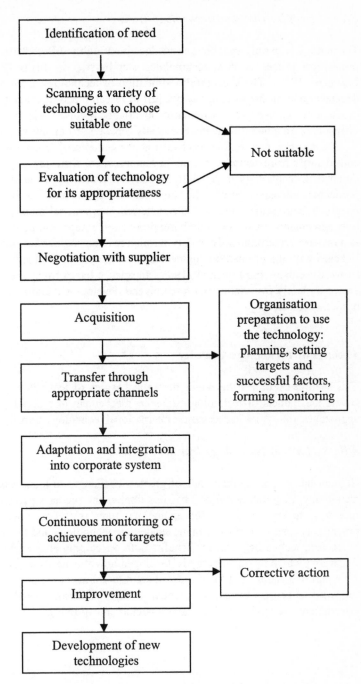

Figure 3.2 Technology transfer process (Ofori, 1994)

Evaluation of International Technology Transfer

Technology is mainly specific knowledge about highly differentiated products and production processes that accumulates step-by-step in firms (Rosenberg and Frischtak, 1985). The successful assimilation of technology from outside sources depends on an in-house capacity not just in research and development, but also in production engineering. Assimilation invariably involves adaptation, so that the diffusion of an innovation cannot be neatly separated from innovation itself.

The sources, nature, and mechanisms of international technology transfer vary considerably from sector to sector. In sectors where firms are in general supplier-dominated, technology is generally already embodied in production machines. In production-intensive firms, the key technology relates to constructing and operating large-scale plant and is transferred international mainly through know-how agreements. In sectors supplying production equipment, however, technology is transferred internationally mainly through reverse engineering and through local linkages with the production engineering departments in production-intensive user firms (Rosenberg and Frischtak, 1985). In science-based firms, the key technology emerges mainly from industrial research and development and in some cases from academic research.

Theories of Technology Transfer

This section examines the major theoretical issues of technology transfer, which covers the models of technology transfer, mechanism of technology transfer and approaches and issues in measuring international technology transfer.

A Basic Model of Technology Transfer

Cultural barriers are perhaps one of greatest challenges to a successful transfer of technology. Penetrating cultural barriers implies the sender's perceptions as to the receivers' needs. As far as the technology transfer is concerned, an important principle is congruence between the sender, the technology and the receiver.

In fact, technology transfer benefits both developing and developed countries. Regarding where the technology is developed how it is utilised who uses it and for what purpose, Samli (1985) considered six dimensions of technology related to the following specific aspects: geography, culture, economy, people, business, and government. He models technology transfer as shown in Figure 3.3.

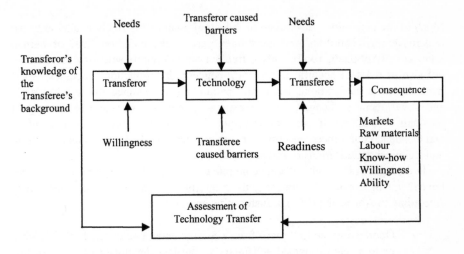

Figure 3.3 A basic model of technology transfer (Samli, 1985)

Product Life Cycle Theory of Technology Transfer

Walsh (1987) suggests that the typical approach of the foreign organisation is to attempt to use familiar technologies rather than develop production process skills of the existing labour force. This approach provides short-term solutions to shortfalls in indigenous capacity and a residue of the imported technology can be expected to remain in the country, contributing to a longer-term improvement in capacity. The extent to which this happens naturally, however, is debatable. Lam (1997) argues that the difficulties in the transfer of knowledge arise not simply from the tacit nature of knowledge itself, but from differences in the degree of tacitness of knowledge and the way in which it formed, structured and utilised in different countries.

Technology transfer has played an important role in the international economy and technological co-operation, the dissemination of science and technology and promotion of international trade. According to Chen, (1994), the importance of technology transfer has been one of the main Chinese aims in attracting foreign investment. The unsophisticated technology transferred to China by foreign firms resonates with the predication suggested by product life cycle theory. The theory states that as the technology of a product becomes more standardised and static, the product migrates to lower-income countries where labour cost becomes a more important basis for comparison than research and development. The Chinese were in the final stage of their cycle, namely the standardised stage, where management skills and labour costs rather than technical skills, were critical (Chen, 1994).

The Mechanisms of Technology Transfer

Much of the technology developed in industrial countries is freely available to the underdeveloped countries and constitutes part of the common fund of human knowledge (Abi-Saab, 1967). This is true not only of purely scientific knowledge, but also of a lot of specific information concerning production processes. Apart from scientific publications, such information can be obtained through academic and government exchanges, foreign experts, scientific and practical training of nationals abroad, etc. It can also be acquired by attending international scientific and technical conferences, meetings or seminars held by the international scientific and technical organisations or institutions.

In the light of the political and economic conditions of the countries concerned, the patterns of transfer of technology from enterprise to enterprise vary enormously. According to Abi-Saab (1967), transfer of technology can be:

- Operated in the first place from a foreign enterprise to one of its branches or to a wholly owned subsidiary in the less developed country. In this case, the transfer of technology is part of direct private foreign investment in that country.
- Arranged by the patentee to sell the use of the process to a producer in the less developed country through a license.
- Operated with 'turn-key' formula. According to which the foreign enterprise undertakes to build all the installations and the machinery necessary for the working of the process. The consideration for the use of the process will be part of the global price.

One basic consideration becomes apparent: as far as technology transfer is concerned, what counts most is not the legal formula employed to effect the transfer, but that it directs foreign investment, licensing or joint venture.

The foreign enterprise may be attracted to the less developed countries by raw materials, cheap labour and access to new markets, but the result will be a dual economy, as exists in many countries. Real implantation may require its adaptation to local conditions, such as climate, availability of factors of production, tastes, etc. In this respect, the foreign staff may learn from their local counterparts as well as teach them. The development of the product on the spot is thus a very important aspect of the successful transfer of technology and its implantation (Ramaer, 1967).

Summary

What has become apparent is that the critical issues of technology transfer between developed and developing countries should be sufficiently addressed. Much has been published about the significance of international technology transfer, but relatively little touches on ensuring the effectiveness or appropriateness of the technology transferred. However, the difficulties in measuring technology transfer lies in that there are two major kinds of knowledge, explicit and tacit. International flow of public technological information (scientific and technological journals, patent descriptions i.e. explicit knowledge) and of firm-specific information (drawings and blueprints, operating manuals), are only part of the process of international technology transfer while the other significant part of knowledge still exists. For example, the transfer of persons or institution-embodied know-how, is even harder to measure as it is kept in the human brain. Furthermore, it has been pointed out by researchers that technology transfer requirement should be specified in a contract with a highly structured system. To date no systematic and theoretic model is available to establish the essential ingredients for this type of transfer.

Chapter 4

Technology Transfer in the Construction Industry in China

Introduction

Following the examination of aspects of the construction industry, this chapter will review the present situation of the construction industry in China. The chapter will touch upon the issues of technology transfer in the construction industry and its internationalisation of construction industry in China. Finally, the chapter will address the issues and options in construction technology transfer.

The Construction Industry

The construction industry plays a major role in economic development in both developed and developing countries with its special characteristics compared with other industries. It undertakes the production of various construction products. In other words, the construction industry involves the construction and reconstruction of housing, infrastructure, the installation of various equipment and facilities, the surveying and designing of various construction products for various material production entities, and non-material production entities of national economy.

Definition of Construction

Construction is a traditional industry, whose background dictates that it has not developed at the same pace as that of other industries (Scott, Ponniah and Saud, 1997). Whether it is justified or not, this industry is often perceived as old fashioned and reluctant to come to terms fully with the modern business world of today. Horner and Zaja (1991) argue that it would be a loss in competitive advantage if new management techniques, such as management know-how, are not properly considered and adopted, no matter how sensible it is that new ideas are not adopted until they have been tried and tested. Raftery *et al.* (1998) review recent developments in the construction industry and identify the major trends that have helped polarise the financial and technical superiority of the developed countries and the corresponding inferiority of the developing countries. Raftery *et al.* (1998) argues that technology transfer, in the long run, could be one of the important ways to fill this gap. Joint venture between multi-national companies and local companies is an effective approach and preferred vehicle.

Role of Construction

The construction industry plays a major role in economic development in the less industrialised nations since it constitutes a significant portion of both gross national product and of employment (Abbott, 1985). Indeed, the creation of physical facilities constitutes more than one half of the gross domestic investment of both developed and developing nations. The construction industry also plays a key role in satisfying a wide range of physical, economic and social needs and contributes significantly to the fulfilment of various major national goals. The industry's size, the nature of its operation, and its presence in every developmental activity make it an attractive area for the transfer, adaptation, and development of technologies consistent with the development goals of emerging nations.

Stages of Development of the Construction Industry

The development of a local construction industry follows economic development fairly closely. Abbott, (1985) identified five basic stages in the development of an indigenous contracting industry as follows:

- Foreign firms play an important role in construction activity. Foreign firms have the expertise and local firms do not, or it may be that local firms do not even exist, except perhaps as informal jobbing contractors.
- Local sub-contractors begin to develop perhaps to take over small parts of the foreign contractor's work. These sub-contractors may be formed by local entrepreneurs, which are able to supply labour.
- Local contractors execute small projects. This is a significant step, for these firms are taking commercial risks and are probably completing projects that foreign contractors are not interested in.
- Local contractors take over most local work. Perhaps by keeping costs down, these firms compete successfully with foreign firms, but they also undertake joint ventures with the foreign firms for larger contracts.
- Local contractors seek new work abroad. Initially this may mean that the contractors bid for work in neighbouring countries but there is also the possibility of bidding for contracts further afield.

It is clear that the relative importance and the demand of technology transfer in this process is demonstrated not just at the joint venture stage, but also earlier, since the transfer stimulates the growth of local contractors and consultants, and there are consequent passes on effects.

The Construction Industry in China

China's economy is now one of the largest in the world. The rapid economic expansion has also created one of the largest construction markets in the world (Bon, 1997). The increase in economic activity has generated and will continue to do so, a heavy demand for construction for at least the next 10 years. Therefore, the heavy demand for construction, caused by the rapid economic growth, cannot be satisfied by China's current resources, either physical, technological or managerial. The construction industry in China has suffered for many years as a result of long construction cycles, inadequate planning and programming of projects and poor quality workmanship. Therefore, an increasing number of construction projects are promoted for international competitive bidding. In this way, not only can advanced technology be introduced, but also advanced management practices and methods can be imported from the advanced countries.

The construction industry in China was not recognised officially as a separate industry until 1983. In the past, it was viewed as a subordinate part of the "Basic Construction" (*jiben jianshe* in Chinese language or government investment). Therefore, the construction industry was regarded as producing no financial value through design and construction activities. The creative and significant contribution of construction industry to the national economy was completely denied. In fact, the construction industry plays a very important role in the national economy.

Another feature of the construction dimension in China is that there is a large increase in externally financed projects. In addition to providing project finance, international funding agencies, such as the World Bank, are keen to address the issues of shortening the gaps between developed and developing countries, namely increasing the future capacity of the indigenous industry to meet the demands placed upon it. The principal vehicle for achieving this is technology transfer.

Private Firms in China's Construction Sector

Economic reform is succeeding in China's construction industry. As a result, China's privately owned construction companies now play an important role in the country's construction sector, which produce 60 percent of its output and account for 85 percent of the sector's profits. So far, more than 13,000, or more than 28 percent, of China's assets- and quality-certified construction firms have undergone structural reforms in accordance with contemporary management standards and practices (*Economic Daily*, 1999). These companies include 1,844 joint-stock corporations, 7,833 limited companies, 1,983 solely state-owned enterprises, 1,167 shareholding co-operative firms, 270 enterprise groups and 23 listed stock companies.

China's private construction companies now generate RMB500 billion (US$60.39 billion) in annual output value, which is 60 percent of the sector's total.

These private firms also produce RMB10.6 billion (US$1.28 billion) in annual profits - a huge 85 percent of the total for the entire construction sector.

Internationalisation of the Construction Industry in China

With the accession to the World Trade Organisation (WTO), and as economic reform takes effect, China is facing both opportunities and challenges. The construction market in China is becoming more and more internationalised. However, the following factors are implications of internationalisation of the construction industry in China.

Increase in the Projects Financed by the World Bank The number of construction projects financed by the World Bank and also by the Asian Development Bank has been increasing since the World Bank recommenced the provision of loans to China at the beginning of the 1980s. So far, the total amount of loans provided by the World Bank to China has exceeded US$20 billion (Sun, 1997). There are about 200 projects financed with a loan from the World Bank, which are widespread in various industries, such as construction, agriculture, transportation, communication, energy, social and educational development, and so on. Some notable examples are: the Lubuge Hydro-electric Power Station, the Ertian Hydro-electric Power Station, the Jing-Jin-Tang Express Way, and the Xiaolangdi Hydro-electric Network.

Project-Contracting Overseas China has made great achievements in the field of international economic and technological co-operation, project contracting in the international construction market. By the end of 1995, there were 578 domestic construction companies in China which were approved and authorised by the Ministry of Foreign Economy and Trade Co-operation to undertake international construction project-contracting and labour service, with a total contract value of US$ 50 billion, a turnover of US$ 32.1 billion, a workforce dispatched to foreign countries of 1.104 million and a business coverage of more than 170 countries in the world (Li, 1997).

Foreign Joint-Venture Investments Since the reform and opening up to the outside world, China has absorbed a large amount of foreign capital through various channels. By the end of 1996, 283,793 foreign investment projects were approved in China, with a total contract value of US$ 469.325 billion and a total value paid up value of US$177.217 billion. More than 140,000 joint ventures are in operation, with a total employment of 17 million (Ma, 1997). There is an increasing number of multi-national firms in the world which are coming to China for investment. Among the top 500 large and multi-national firms in the world, more than 200 have made investments in China. There are 132 large multi-national firms, which have established offices in Beijing alone. Technology-concentrated projects have increased because of the coming of the large and multi-national firms. With the establishment of many Sino-foreign joint-ventures, investment has been brought in and greatly increased the number of infrastructure projects, such as expressways, water plants, cement plants, power plants; commercial facilities, such as, department stores, shopping centres, as well as high standard multi-function buildings.

Investment Overseas   At the same time, China has made a large amount of investment in various countries in the world through its multi-national companies. A lot of companies set up their factories and built facilities in many countries in the world. For example, China State Construction Engineering Corporation (CSCEC), the largest construction company in China, with 22,000 employees, 8 branch companies, 6 design institutes, 1 technical school and 1 training centre, 35 regional branches and 8 specialist branches, has established 63 overseas branches and offices and made investments in many countries all over the world (Flanagan and Li, 1997).

Technology Transfer in the Construction Industry

The international construction industry has long been involved with different forms of technology transfer (Abbott, 1985). For many companies, whether they are consulting engineers, engineering design organisations or contractors, technology transfer is just a new term used to describe the training element in foreign construction that they have often had to undertake.

The rising demand from public and private clients in developing countries, however, supported by the international aid organisations for a technology transfer element in contracts let to foreign companies, has led to a new pre-occupation with its definition and implementation.

Construction Technology Transfer Vehicles

During the process of technology transfer, the transferor does not always provide the transferee with solutions to specific problems. As a matter of fact, an effective transfer occurs when technology is requested, transmitted, received, understood, applied, diffused widely and improved. Ofori, (1994) models the construction technology transfer vehicles in Figure 4.1.

Source   Vehicle   Recipient   Post-reception

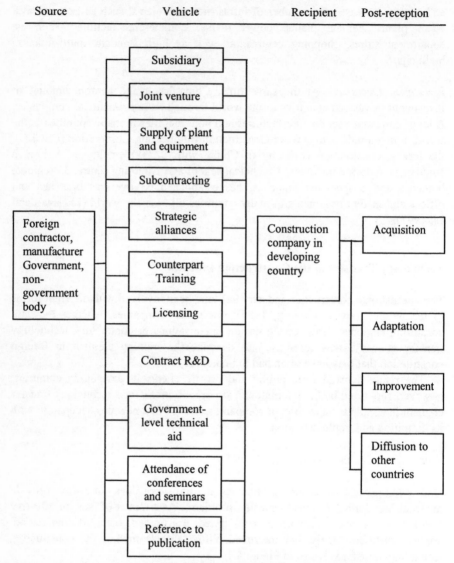

Figure 4.1 Construction technology transfer vehicles (Ofori, 1994)

This has outlined the major elements that appear during the process of international technology transfer.

Identification of Appropriate Construction Technology

The suggestions of the World Bank (1979) for the identification of more appropriate construction technologies and techniques have established grounding, which are:

- *Appropriateness of goal.* Does the technology support the goals of development policy?
- *Appropriateness of product.* Is the final product or service delivered, useful, acceptable and affordable to the intended users?
- *Appropriateness of process.* Does the production process make economic use of inputs?
- *Cultural and environmental appropriateness.* Are the production processes, the products delivered and the institutional arrangements compatible with the local environmental and cultural settings (The World Bank, 1976).

A United Nation Development Programme (UNDP) study for determining the most appropriate construction technologies and techniques has listed the following criteria (UNDP/World Bank, 1979):

- Amount of local labour incorporated - objective to maximise
- Amount of indigenous material used - objective to maximise
- Functional performance
- Replicability
- Capital cost
- Life cycle cost
- Time to implement
- Amount of foreign exchange component - objective to minimise
- Environmental impact
- Social impact
- Economic impact

Patterns of International Trade in Construction

Bon (1997) believes that in terms of national economy the countries can be considered in three categories:

- Advanced industrialised countries (AIC);
- Newly industrialised countries (NIC);
- Less developed countries (LDC).

Based upon the above premises and international survey of construction, Bon (1997) models the present pattern of international trade and technology transfer in construction services as shown in Figure 4.2. The arrows in the figure show the direction of current patterns of trade in construction services.

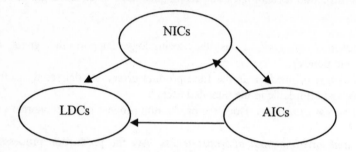

Figure 4.2 Present pattern of trade in construction services (Bon, 1997)

It should be noticed that evidence from India, Turkey and South Korea support the pattern. China is another example. Since the economic reform in 1978, the Chinese construction industry has played an important role in the international construction market by dispatching construction forces not only to LDC, such as African countries but also AIC, such as European countries and America.

A large proportion of construction activity remains local, regional or national at all stages of development. The segment of the construction sector that engages in multinational, continental, or global construction activity may be growing. The global market in construction services is far from restricted to advanced industrialised countries. Both less developed countries and newly developed countries already play important parts in the global market (Drewer, 1990). At present, advanced industrialised countries may continue providing highly specialised construction services to newly industrialised countries and less developed countries. These services may focus on high-technology or capital-intensive project, as well as on highly specialised maintenance and repair construction, which is growing in advanced industrialised countries (Bon, 1996). Technology transfer from the advanced industrialised countries is likely to be based around professional expertise being transferred to the newly industrialised countries and less developed countries. Indeed in 1993, the World Bank adopted an explicit policy of assistance to promote the growth of borrower countries in construction industries (Langford, 1995).

Construction Technology Transfer: Issues and Options

This section will address the different attitude of governments, the attitude of the World Bank in terms of international technology transfer in construction and the barriers to technology transfer in construction.

Attitude of the Governments

Governments everywhere (and especially in the developing countries), have sought to control, guide and encourage technology transfer through various means which were summarised by Ofori (1992) as follows:

- Training components are made mandatory in joint-venture agreements between foreign and local partners, in terms of engagement of foreign companies for construction projects or in agreements for direct investment by manufacturing enterprises.
- Guidelines for licensing agreements are formulated and administered which prohibit the transfer of certain technologies, outline prices or pricing mechanisms or suggest terms of contract.
- Support is provided for technical information and extension services to facilitate the diffusion of technologies.

Attitude of the World Bank

The World Bank encourages technology transfer in the construction industry and favours the formation of joint ventures, which appear to be the most widely preferred vehicle of technology transfer in construction. In addition, public, private sector clients, and leading agencies have supported technology transfer in the construction industry. For example, as far as the Xiaolangdi Multi-purpose Dam Project[1] is concerned, as a condition of providing loan to the Chinese government, the World Bank strongly suggests (WB, 1994):

- To establish a project management organisation which has the ability to raise funding and manage the project independently.
- To establish a management system, with which the project management team is able to clarify the relationships between the rights and the responsibilities of the Client, Engineer and the Contractors.
- To make clear that the contracts could be awarded to the well established Sino-foreign joint-venture contractors so as to create the best international practice and obtain technology transfer and exchange of technology.

---

[1] Xiaolangdi Multi-purpose Dam Project, across the Yellow River in Henan Province, P.R.C., was jointly funded by the World Bank and the Central Government. It is quoted by the Chinese Government as a demonstration project for international project management of Sino-foreign joint ventures. The project, chosen as a, will be further explained in later chapters.

Barriers to Technology Transfer

There appears to be more resistance to technology transfer in construction than in other industries. The barriers in transfer of construction technology as identified by Abbott (1985) include:

- Unwillingness of foreign firms to nurture potential competitors in a declining world market.
- Tendency of technology transfer to add a time and cost element (and managerial complexity) to the already difficult and risky business of contracting.
- The usual lack of understanding (among foreign enterprises, local beneficiaries and clients) of what is to be transferred.
- Suspicion of the recipient and the client about usefulness of what is being transferred.
- Ineffectiveness of previous transfer, as the trained personnel seldom utilise what they learn.

The Current Situation of Technology Transfer in China

Before the economic reform of 1978, construction industry and other industries in China were arranged in a 'block' format (Flanagan and Li, 1997), where they each had the same factories making the same products for the customers with the same demands. The reform from the central planned economy to the market economy saw the break down of these blocks and Chinese firms were suddenly faced with international competition. They had to absorb technology that helps them survive. As a result, technology transfer has become very important and popular in China.

China's leader, *Deng Xiaoping*,[2] has set targets to achieve a per capita income of US$4000 (presumably at 1987 prices) by 2049 - the Hundredth Anniversary of Communist rule - which would rank China among the medium-developed countries in the world. To achieve this will involve both the importation and absorption of foreign technology on an unprecedented scale.

Legal Status of Technology Transfer

Since economic reform started in 1978, issues of international technology transfer in China have been highly regarded. At present, the priority of this work is to

---

[2] *Deng Xiaoping* (1904-1997), Chinese Communist leader who served as the *de facto* ruler of China from 1976 to 1997. Under Deng, who survived two purges before he succeeded Mao Zedong, China developed into one of the fastest-growing economies in the world.

introduce new and advanced technology from developed countries and in the meantime to export the advanced technology as well. In order to promote international technology transfer, several relevant laws and regulations have been worked out, such as, the Technology Contract Law of China adopted in 1987, the Science and Technology Improvement Law of China adopted in 1993, and the Science and Technology Result Transfer Law of China adopted in 1996 (Yu, 1991). It should be noted that these laws and policies have had a profound influence on technology transfer in China. In addition, technology transfer has been one of the main Chinese objectives in attracting foreign investment.

Encouragement of Technology Transfer

The Science and Technology Improvement Law of China encourages enterprises to carry out technological innovation and the renewal of equipment so as to increase scientific and management competence. This law facilitates enterprises to develop new technology and to strengthen competitive power in the market, in line with the demand of the international and domestic market. Enterprises are encouraged to import advanced technology and equipment from developed countries through technology consultation, where they can develop new products and high-technology products by applying new technology to participate in the competitve international market and to promote the internationalisation of high-technology industry.

The improvement of science and technology in industry, communication, post and telecommunication, geological prospecting, construction and installation should always be encouraged so as to increase the economic and social results.

Aspects of International Technology Transfer in China's Construction Industry

In the process of the internationalisation of the construction market in China, technology transfer is most likely to be involved in the following respects:

Training Services in Project Management

Since 1988, a supervision system has been introduced for the execution of large and middle-sized construction projects. A large number of construction supervision companies were established. Construction supervisors were trained so as to promote the construction supervision system. However, there still exist many problems in the process of the execution of project supervision. Supervisors need to be familiar with international practices and to be trained to have a good command of the basic theory of project supervision. The means and methods need to be improved with wide application of computer technology and information technology. Therefore, the potential exists for western consultants to provide project supervision management services in China.

In early 1990, the introduction of a project-client's responsibility system led to training opportunity as well. Since 1992, medium and large-sized projects must have a project client who has responsibility for the execution of the project from "grass root" to "turn key" to ensure a good investment and economicreturn. To do the work well still needs a large quantity of experienced personnel.

Joint-venture Operation

In the construction market in China, construction activities can be organised in collaboration with a foreign construction contractor, with whom the Chinese construction contractor enters into an agreement. Generally, this option is allowed when advanced technology and management skills from international contractors are required for major complex foreign investment projects.

Consulting Services

Foreign consulting companies are invited to provide consulting services on projects with international funding. In the preliminary stage of the Xiaolangdi Hydro-electric Network, for example, a contract was awarded to a leading Canadian consulting company for the consulting services of a feasibility study.

High and New Technology Based Projects

Foreign general contractors have been independently employed in China frequently on "high tech" turn key projects. The joint-venture investment project of the China World Trade Centre in Beijing was signed in 1986. The project is a US$231 million hotel, office and apartment complex. The contract for the first two phases of the project was awarded to a leading French general contractor, Société Auxiliare d'Entreprises (SAE). One of the main obligations of the contractor was to employ Chinese workers and provide technical training to Chinese specialist trade contractors.

Projects Financed by the World Bank

In most cases, the projects financed with a loan from the World Bank are promoted for international competitive bidding. The Xiaolangdi Hydro-electric Network, the largest construction project financed in China with loans from the World Bank, is a model project of the World Bank and the Chinese government. The contract value of the first phase of the project is about RMB32 billion (about US$4 billion). Three major joint-venture companies, including a Sino-French, a Sino-German and a Sino-Italy joint ventures were involved in the execution of the project.

Summary

Technology Transfer: Problems and Solutions

It is clear that confusions about technology transfer in the construction industry can be attributed not only to a misunderstanding of the concept, but also to the complexities of comprehending the transferee's needs and formulating programmes that effectively satisfy these needs. Therefore, satisfactory measures of ensuring technology transfer is still a hard task due to a lack of appropriate data and clear definition as well as the complexity of the process and channels through which technology is transferred.

A Framework of Technology Transfer in Construction

Based on the review of the current literature of technology transfer in construction and the premises of technology transfer models, an attempt has been made for the establishment of a framework of technology transfer in construction. It should be pointed out that it is impossible that this framework will be applicable and functional to all relevant situations. However, the model presented here will provide insights into the key components of technology transfer in construction. The failure or success of technology transfer rests on the congruence of all the parties concerned. Furthermore, the responsibility for technology transfer should fall jointly on the funding agency, the transferor, and the transferee as well as the congruence among all the parties regarding the technology to be transferred as shown in Figure 4.3.

In this framework, a principle has been addressed that is important in the process of technology transfer in the construction industry, namely congruence among the transferor, transferee and the funding agency regarding the technology to be transferred. Among all the relevant parties, if a high degree of congruence does not exist, the technology will not be transferred effectively. It should be pointed out that there exists a deference towards technology transfer between public funded projects and private funded projects. Technology transfer is promoted in the projects funded by governmental agencies and developmental agencies such as the World Bank and the Asian Development Bank. However, there is difference in terms of technology transfer as far as the private funded project is concerned.

Current Issues of Technology Transfer in China

The construction industry in China still displays characteristics of its origin in a planned economy. However, its structure is not uniform and in fact presents quite a complex picture. There are state-owned units, nominally collective-owned units which are in fact also owned by the state and true collective-owned units run by rural construction teams. Overlaid upon these rather anachronist organisations, are new generations of construction companies, which can be wholly owned by Chinese organizations, owned by a foreign organisation or a joint-venture between the two. An irony of the situation is that the most traditional rural construction teams composed of peasants from agricultural production often out-perform more technically-superior companies as pointed out by the *Economy Daily*. This is because significant inefficiencies have developed, where the industry has attempted to keep pace with rapid economic expansion by transplanting new technology without the capacity to fully embrace it. It is this sector of the industry that is struggling to come to terms with technology and this will be the focus of this study.

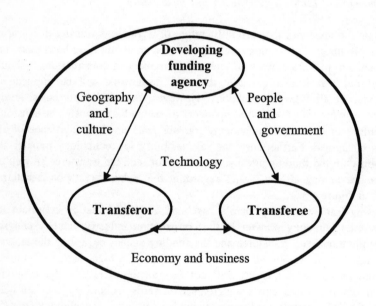

Figure 4.3 Technology transfer within good congruence

Chapter 5

Theory and Practice of Knowledge Transfer

Introduction

The review of the current literature of technology transfer suggests that technology transfer may be ineffective or subordinated by other issues of which knowledge transfer is the most significant as knowledge is the key to control over technology as a whole. A further examination of the current literature of technology transfer shows that interest in knowledge transfer is at present more popular than in technology transfer. Sometimes, technology transfer and knowledge transfer go hand in hand. Sometimes, knowledge transfer occurs without technology transfer. In most cases, it is knowledge that flows between the transferor and the transferee. Without knowledge transfer, technology transfer does not work.

First of all, this chapter addresses issues of communication and knowledge transfer in the construction industry, with particular reference to international joint-venture projects. Based upon the survey of the literature of knowledge transfer, this chapter reports problems and practicalities of knowledge transfer with a particular examination of various aspects of knowledge transfer in the process of problem-solving and decision-making within joint-venture projects. The strength of any project decision is based on the knowledge, expertise and project information that informs those making the decision. The potential for decision-making and problem-solving is held within the knowledge and expertise of the project team.

Communication and Knowledge Transfer

Communication is a relatively recent academic discipline, and organisational communication has been an important subject of that discipline since 1950. Communication is acknowledged by academics and managers as a major push since 1970 to develop instruments helpful in analysing communication so that we can make interventions to achieve organisational effectiveness (Downs, 1994). Communication is a process involving the exchange of messages and the creation of meaning, and requires that at least two people contribute to the ongoing and dynamic sequence of events in which each affects and is affected by the other in a system of reciprocal determination (Gudykunst, 1998; Hargie, 1994). Therefore, without effective communication, it would be impossible to achieve a successful knowledge transfer.

Communication Issues in Construction

Without delving into the intricacies of semantics and linguistics, it is clear that communication, even on the most fundamental level, poses certain issues. *A* sends a simple message to *B*. Did *B* understand *A*? If not, does *A* realise that *B* has misinterpreted the message? How often does an individual, especially in non-verbal communication, read a message incorrectly?

No doubt the most efficient way to communicate information from one person to another is orally, face to face. As Austen and Neale (1995) point out, this form of communication is more efficient because it does not just rely on words: gestures, eye contact and other forms of non-verbal communication are used. Furthermore, the communication process relies on interaction between people. Other forms of informal communication include telephone conversations and hand-written notes, both of which are effective.

This is especially the case in construction. In construction, specifications are written in a logical, orderly manner to describe the quality of the workmanship, the quality of the material, and the descriptive features of the project. As a matter of fact, the specifications communicate those aspects of the job best described with words while the drawings communicate those aspects of physical details, locations and dimensions. Due to the technical sophistication of the message, communication in construction is seen as a sort of modern hieroglyphics like translating a foreign language (Melvin, 1979). However, construction management requires germane skills of communication that touches every one in diverse forms. Essentially, that is what construction management is all about: several groups communicating with each other in the joint-venture teamwork of building a structure.

Knowledge Management in Construction

It is widely recognised that knowledge management is an important issue in construction industry. Literature suggests various definitions for knowledge management. However, Egbu (2000) defines knowledge management as:

> Knowledge management is about the process by which knowledge is created, acquired, communicated, shared, applied and effectively utilised and managed in order to meet existing and emerging needs, to identify and exploit existing and acquired knowledge assets.

From an organisational perspective, effective knowledge management is about turning personal knowledge into corporate knowledge that can be widely shared and properly applied throughout the organisation in such a way as to create competitive advantage to the organisation.

and properly applied throughout the organisation in such a way as to create competitive advantage to the organisation.

It is regarded as a subject that suggests that what we have in our minds, for example, intellectual capital, intellectual property, experience, knowledge and information, is our primary commercial resource (Steward, 1998). Frappaolo and Toms (1997) define knowledge management as a tool-set for the automation of deductive or inherent relationships between information objects, users and processes while Takeuchi (1998) believes that knowledge management is about capturing knowledge gained by individuals and spreading it to others in the organisation. However, the development of knowledge management as a discipline gives us the opportunity to model the dynamic interpersonal process of knowledge transfer. Furthermore, such discussion can help increase the profile of "people-centred" strategic thinking.

Egbu (2000) argues that lower costs and higher productivity are no longer seen as key influences on long term corporate competitiveness. There is no doubt that to a great extent they ensure survival but not growth. The ever-changing markets and the nature of competition also demand accelerated innovation and knowledge creation supported by the dynamic core capabilities of organisations. There is an increasing acceptance that the economic and producing power of a modern organisation relies more on its intellectual and service capability than in its hard assets, such as land, plant and equipment. Effective knowledge management is seen as offering market leverage and competitive advantage to organisations.

Knowledge management is a complex social process. Egbu (2000) further argues that knowledge management is 10 percent technology and 90 percent people issues. Knowledge management is sophisticated not only because of its potential for organisational value but also because of the solutions and technologies that can be applied to it. It is the role of knowledge management, therefore, to connect two nodes, knowledge owners and knowledge seekers. The knowledge of one is transferred to the mind of another, so that a new decision can be made or situation handled.

Explicit Knowledge and Tacit Knowledge

Knowledge is increasingly being recognised as a vital organisational resource that gives market leverage and competitive advantage (Nonaka and Taekuchi, 1995; Leonard-Barton, 1995). Knowledge consists of truth, beliefs, perspectives, concepts, judgements, expectations, methodologies and know-how, and exists in different forms such as tacit, explicit, symbolic, embodied, embrained and encultured knowledge. In particular, knowledge has become a substance to be "managed" at its most literal sense. Polanyi (1967) considered human knowledge by starting from the fact that *we know more than we can tell*. In general, knowledge consists of two components, namely explicit and tacit. Technical knowledge consists of these two components – 'explicit' and 'tacit', however, the greater the extent to which a technology exists in the form of the softer, less physical resources, the greater the proportion of tacit knowledge it contains. Tacit knowledge, due to its non-codifiable nature has to be transferred through 'intimate human interactions' (Tsang, 1997).

Features of Explicit and Tacit Knowledge

Nonaka and Takeuchi (1995) describe some distinctions between tacit and explicit knowledge, which are shown in Table 5.1. Features generally associated with the more tacit aspects of knowledge are shown on the left, while the corresponding qualities related to explicit knowledge are shown on the right. Knowledge of experience tends to be tacit, physical, and subjective, while knowledge of rationality tends to be explicit, metaphysical, and objective. Tacit knowledge is created "here and now" in a specific, practical context, while explicit knowledge is about past events or objects "there and then". Table 5.1 shows the features of explicit and tacit knowledge.

Tacit Knowledge Subjective	Explicit Knowledge Objective
Knowledge of experience (body) Simultaneous knowledge (here and now) Analogy knowledge (practice)	Knowledge of rationality (mind) Sequential knowledge (there and then) Digital knowledge (theory)

Table 5.1 Features of tacit knowledge and explicit knowledge (Nonaka and Takeuchi, 1995)

Model of Codification of Knowledge

Skyrme (1999) models the packaging and commercialising knowledge, which shows some form of codification from tacit knowledge to knowledge in more explicit forms. What starts as un-codified knowledge, often a set of ideas, is gradually shaped through interaction and expression into something more tangible, such as a process description, a product design or specification, which finally emerges as products for the market. Figure 5.1 represents the model of codification of knowledge.

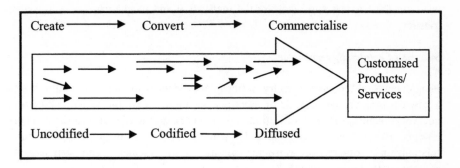

Figure 5.1 Codification of knowledge (Skyrme, 1999)

Knowledge Transfer

Knowledge transfer is about getting the right knowledge to the right people at the right time. Knowledge transfer is about connection not collection, and that connection ultimately depends on the choice made by individuals (Dougherty, 1999). It is worth noting that this form of transfer in particular may well be a "two-way process" between the transferor and the transferee. Knowledge transfer is also an increasingly popular term in the literature as writers attempt to highlight the human aspect of knowledge management. There is often a distinction made between knowledge transfer that occurs naturally or informally, and that which takes place in more formalised routines.

This natural transfer, or unstructured exchanges and informal exchanges, are vital to a firm's success. However, one of the essential elements of knowledge management and knowledge transfer is to develop special strategies to encourage such spontaneous exchanges of knowledge (Davenport and Prusak, 1998). It is of great significance for an organisation to be able to capture and use the knowledge inside managers' heads. Maitland (1999) argues that the crucial factor in determining a company's competitive advantage is its ability to convert tacit knowledge into explicit knowledge through organisational learning. That is why some companies encourage friendly networking and the release of tacit knowledge by setting up individual intranet sites where staff can post information about themselves.

Problems and Practicalities in Knowledge Transfer

What has become apparent is that confusion about knowledge transfer can be attributed not only to a misunderstanding of the concept, but also to the complexities of comprehending the transferee's needs and formulating programmes that effectively satisfy these needs. This section addresses a range of issues of knowledge transfer, such as how to achieve success in knowledge transfer, what are the barriers and what are the motivation and mechanisms of knowledge transfer.

Success of Knowledge Transfer

People's natural tendency is to try to transplant the work in their home culture into a new culture. To the surprise of most people, these "tried and tested" skills will not work, resulting in destabilisation, culture shock and intolerance towards others (Berger, 1998). It is necessary to understand the basic tenet of good cross-cultural relationships, otherwise, misunderstanding may escalate and barriers to communication may be erected.

The significance of global thinking has been widely promoted over the past five to ten years, yet it has not impacted on the learning of managerial skills. Cultural awareness and country briefings have been highly evaluated in the staff development plans of many enterprises. However, what is needed is a more integrated approach blending skills to recognise the cultural context when planning a strategy to build effective relationships and systems. There is no magic for people to develop in terms of cross-cultural skills. However, Berger (1998) has listed the following skills for developing a successful knowledge transfer:

Communication Communication is a process by which people verbalise their feelings, express their opinions, convey their ideas, influence others and transmit knowledge. Without communication civilisation would spin into a spiral of confusion and chaos. Communication skills include:

- Gauging one's level of jargon and speed of delivery to the language fluency of the listener;
- Recognising the differing cultural meanings of verbal and non-verbal behaviour;
- Listening and questioning to understand the views and opinions of others;
- Awareness of what is expected at the initial stage of building a relationship in order to build sufficient trust to work together productively.

Behavioural Expectation Behavioural Expectation includes:

- Alertness to how people expect to behave at meetings, including preparation and agenda management;
- Awareness of a style of leading, negotiating and breaking deadlocks which is appropriate to a given culture;
- Recognition of how decisions are taken by another culture and the implication for time management and how decisions are taken.

Cultural Value Based upon his survey, Hofstede (1993) concludes:

- Knowing which cultural values are most likely to impact on business, for example, leadership and decision-making style, importance of structure, individualistic compared to collectivist style of relationships and the importance of time;
- Preparedness to adopt to cultures whose values are different from one's own.

Cross-Culture Team Building Learning is defined as the process by which one acquires new information, habits, and abilities. Some psychologists define learning as the essentially permanent modification of behaviour that originates from human interaction with surroundings. Learning networks are used to bring people together from different background to exchange practical ideas which may eventually result in innovative practices in companies (Kululanga, 1997). Transfer of knowledge and skills is an act of power, a claim on time and resources that was considered to be a natural part of organisational order (Darrah, 1995). Joint-ventures between multi-national and local contractors are widely recognised as a means of enhancing local expertise (Glass and Saggi, 1999). As a matter of fact, joint ventures in construction involve even more intimate human interaction between partners, which makes more critical the issues of cross-cultural team building in the process of interaction of both foreign and local partners.

Exchange of Information and Knowledge

A problem with business communication is that people cannot be forced to provide or accept knowledge. The project environment is often filled with complexity increasing with the number of specialists involved. For example, project participants will determine how much effort they are going to expend assisting the processing of information. The individual may be selective with the amount of information disclosed, the person to whom they disclose it and the degree to which they attempt to get the other person to understand. A project environment that facilitates the release and exchange of information needs to support individuals and groups and assist information flow (Egbu *et al*, 2000). Organisations and joint-venture partners need to reduce barriers and support positive communication. Some of the barriers are obvious, but it is probably the less obvious ones that are most threatening to the management of knowledge.

Barriers in Joint-Venture Organisations

With the information and knowledge that flow across international joint-venture organisational boundaries, barriers to communication are often present in the multi-organisational projects (Egbu *et al*, 2000). The interactions of the partners in the projects allow information to be shared. The project teams confer developing common goals, building and sharing information. The motivation is that both parties share a vision of a future where their co-operation will continue, and they are both interested in improving the quality of their relationship. Therefore, short-term one-off projects are often problematic.

The construction industry normally pulls together project teams for one-off and short-term projects. International joint ventures are, in particular, established for a specific project. Little effort is made to develop common objectives, little time is allowed to break down barriers and form strong relationships across which information can flow. Time is a precious resource and the parties see no advantage in building close relationships with companies with which they will probably have no dealings after completion of the current project. Therefore, under the commercial pressures of completing a project to time, quality and cost, it is not always feasible to undertake a formalised commitment to transfer knowledge.

Motivation for Knowledge Transfer

In any interaction people will have their personal objectives or needs, and these needs are likely to vary from situation to situation. The most common reason for people coming together and engaging in interpersonal behaviour is simply that they have to complete some specified task (Hayes, 1994). People working on the same service line will need to converse with each other to get their work done. Therefore, managers in the joint-ventures have to be involved in significant amounts of social interaction and knowledge transfer not because they particularly want to, but because they have to: once social interaction does occur then other motivating factors will come into play (Garavan, 1997).

Mechanisms of Transferring Tacit Knowledge

When knowledge is tacit, its transfer is more difficulty to achieve and monitor. Transfer of tacit knowledge involves intimate human interaction between the transferor and the transferee. Mustapha (1998) argues that this is especially the case in the construction industry because the special nature of the industry makes its management more complicated. This type of knowledge is not amenable to systematic codification and could only be accessed and transferred through intimate social interactions (Kogut and Zander, 1992). Knowledge is utilised and transferred through intensive and extensive interaction between group members. Co-ordination is achieved through mutual adaptation among members with common knowledge and shared implicit coding schemes accumulated through group interactions. Knowledge is generated and stored almost organically in team relationships and the mode of co-ordination is human-network based (Lam, 1997).

Badaracco (1991) identified that there is an expectation that technological partnership and knowledge transfer would enable the partners to take advantage of the complementarities of each other's knowledge and expertise to achieve benefits and raise their competitiveness in the global market. Societal culture is important in affecting the efficacy of technology transfer (Koizumi, 1982; Samli, 1985 and Kedia and Bhagat, 1988). According to Hofstede (1980), and Hofstede and Bond (1988), the absorptive capacity of the recipient for technology transfer is influenced by five dimensions of culture (uncertainty of avoidance, individualism vs. collectivism, power distance, masculinity vs. femininity and Confucian dynamism). This is in particular the case in an environment of Confucian dynamics and culture.

Joint-venture – A Vehicle of Knowledge Transfer

It has been identified that international joint-ventures between domestic companies in developing countries and multi-national firms in developed countries have become a popular means for both management teams to satisfy their objectives. According to Miller (1997), local partners bring knowledge of the domestic market, familiarity with government bureaucracies and regulations, and understanding of local labour markets. Foreign partners can offer advanced process and product technologies, management know-how and access to export market. Therefore, international joint ventures are accepted as the preferred vehicle for transfer of knowledge. In the construction industries of developing countries, joint-ventures between foreign multinationals and local contractors are widely recognised as a means of enhancing local expertise (Glass and Saggi, 1999).

Joint-ventures are an example of collaborative arrangements that can be turned into value-creating mechanisms to graft together competencies and value-creating disciplines of their partners (Miller, 1997). Joint-ventures in construction involve fairly intimate human interaction between partners. These are referred to in this study as "dyadic interactions". A dyad is a set comprising two individuals. The importance of human interactions in the transfer of "tacit" knowledge or "know-how" has already been noted, and it is perhaps because of their potential in this respect that joint-ventures are accepted by many as the preferred vehicle for transfer.

This is confirmed by a survey of joint venture construction companies carried out for the International Section of the Chinese Construction Ministry (Wu, 1998). The most regularly-cited aims of local Chinese partners (after "increasing the profits of the enterprise") were:

- Learning more advanced construction technology.
- Obtaining project management skills.
- Obtaining channels to the international construction market.

Elements of technology transfer also figured among the aims of the foreign partners, with expressions such as "learning how to operate projects in China" rating relatively high after "promoting increased business for the enterprise" and "obtaining profit". This potential is recognised by the World Bank (Carrillo, 1996). In 1993 the Bank adopted an explicit policy of requiring a commitment to technology transfer from its contractors to the construction industries of the host country (Langford, 1995). According to Abbott (1985), an essential condition for effecting such technology transfer is the clear specification of the requirement in a contract. Accordingly, the World Bank's policy was that organisations should not be awarded contracts without them forming meaningful partnerships with local companies (Carrillo, 1993).

Joint-ventures in construction involve fairly intimate human interaction between partners. Problem-solving is predicated on a particular way of making sense of the world (Athey, 1974; Robertshaw, Mecca, and Rerick, 1978; Vangundy, 1988). It frames situations as amenable to a rational process of resolution, one in which careful planning precedes action (Suchman, 1987). As Poon and Price (1999) expected in their study, most of the decisions generally made were of a technical and engineering (64.7 per cent) and financial (28.6 per cent) nature. Personnel decisions were relatively infrequent particularly at low levels. The professionals would need more time to deal more with financial problems while front line supervisors were concentrated mainly on technical and engineering matters. Important decision-making has to involve managers from both sides of joint-venture partners.

Knowledge Management Programmes in Construction

Construction organisations need to recognise the importance of an active process management of knowledge creation, gathering, storing and exploitation. The culture and climate and the mechanisms in place should allow for the possibility for knowledge to be readily shared and transferred from project to project and across project teams (Egbu et al, 1998b, 1998c). Regular meetings, in-house seminars and workshops interviewing, writing, video communication, de-briefing after end of projects, coaching and job rotation are the mechanisms which construction organisation can use for transferring knowledge across project teams. Holland, (1999) suggests ten ways to embed knowledge management into organisational culture:

- Reward knowledge–sharing behaviour.
- Define and communicate knowledge management behaviour.
- Consider formal agreements on knowledge management for key positions.
- Make knowledge management company policy.
- Have managers systematically enforce and reinforce knowledge management.
- Identify knowledge management positions.
- Incentivise key knowledge management actions.
- Explicitly manage knowledge management for each and every employee.
- Publicly recognise good knowledge management.
- Take action on poor knowledge management.

For the development of knowledge management programmes in the construction organisation, based on the Case Study research projects funded by the Economic and Social Research Council (ESRC) and the European Social Fund (ESF), Egbu (2000) has developed a framework for addressing knowledge management issues in construction, where he considers five integrated dimensions in order to develop coherent knowledge management programmes. They are knowledge content, people, processes, and the technological infrastructure culture (leadership, strategy, motivation and communication).

- Content. Defining the knowledge that is strategically relevant to the organisation (knowledge that meets the business needs of the organisation, now and in the future) should be seen as the first step in knowledge management implementation.
- People. Ensuring that key personnel have access to know-how and best practices can enhance knowledge sharing. In addition, efficient and accurate mapping of knowledge can be accomplished with the help of people who informally act as the organisation's memory.
- Culture. The knowledge transfer media chosen by the organisation must be such that is appropriate to its culture.
- Process. An organisation should identify the knowledge, which it has after defining the knowledge it needs. If requisite knowledge is not available within the organisation, then this must be generated, perhaps by acquisition. The introduction of knowledge management needs to follow a logical sequence of tasks to minimise effort and cost.
- Infrastructure and technology. The infrastructure that is put in place to support knowledge management must be adapted to the organisation's needs and not the other way round. It must also specify updating responsibilities, data structure, access rights and security since knowledge gets old and can 'decline in value' over time.

Summary

Effective transfer of knowledge creates value for the construction organisation and their clients, and involves due consideration of the people, content, culture, process and infrastructure dimensions. However, it is an arduous task to achieve because of the sophistication of knowledge creation and knowledge transfer. A further examination of the literature has revealed that there is very little empirical study directed towards knowledge transfer and knowledge management in construction. Therefore, there is ample scope for research in this important area.

It is important to have identified the two major elements of knowledge, explicit knowledge and tacit knowledge. What is more, the identification of both explicit knowledge and tacit knowledge will not only clarify the confusion of mechanisms of knowledge transfer, but also provide significant aid for the tracking of the knowledge transfer process.

Chapter 6

A World Bank Financed Project in China: Xiaolangdi

Introduction

Based upon the current state of understanding of international technology transfer, the chapter presents a theoretic framework for knowledge transfer, where the problem area of knowledge transfer in the current practice has been identified. Therefore, the Case Study is, however, to further define the problem areas and seek solutions. Following a brief introduction of the Xiaolangdi Project in Henan Province, P.R.C., with a particular examination of why the Xiaolangdi Project was chosen as the Case Study for the current research, the chapter reviews the whole arrangement of the pilot study with six study trips to China over two years. Furthermore, the chapter analyses and discusses the data collected during the Case Study. Finally the chapter presents the findings of the Case Study.

Problem Area: From Technology Transfer to Knowledge Transfer

Mnaas (1990) states that technology consists of four closely inter-linked elements: namely, technique, knowledge, organisation and product. However, knowledge contributes the major part to technology, *which is the key to control over technology as a whole*. Technical knowledge consists of two important components - "explicit" (codified in blueprints, designs, drawings and specifications) and "tacit" (kept in the human brain). The greater the extent to which a technology exists in the form of the softer, less physical resources, the greater the proportion of tacit knowledge it contains.

It is important that the understanding of explicit and tacit elements of knowledge will help identify the process of knowledge transfer. With regarding to the appropriateness and effectiveness of technology transfer, Samli (1985) models the pattern of technology transfer with consideration of six dimensions: geography, culture, economy, business, people and government (refer to Figure 3.3). In addressing knowledge transfer issues in construction, Egbu (2000) advanced similar ideas on what he called "a framework for managing knowledge," where he emphasises five dimensions, namely, people, content, culture, process, infrastructure and technology. It should be noted that the above research work has provided wider understanding and significant insights towards the building of an effective and applicable framework of knowledge transfer of the current research project. However, a framework for the establishment of effective knowledge transfer shown as Figure 6.1 has been developed based upon the major contribution of the above research work. It should be pointed out that this framework combines the elements of both technology transfer and knowledge transfer, where the significance of tacit knowledge transfer has been established and the blockage issue of tacit knowledge transfer has been raised.

The Xiaolangdi Project

The Xiaolangdi Hydro-electric Network across the Yellow River in Henan Province, P.R.C., was chosen as the Case Study, not only because it is a key Chinese national project, one of the largest joint venture projects in China, jointly funded by the World Bank and the Central Government of P.R.C., but also because it is quoted by the Chinese government as a demonstration project for international project management of Sino-foreign joint ventures in China.

The Xiaolangdi Hydro-electric Network is located in the last gorge in the middle reach of the Yellow River, about 40 km north of Luoyang City, 130 km downstream of Sanmenxia Dam, and 128 km upstream of Huayuankou in Zhengzhou City. It is the only reservoir with a large storage capacity on the main stem of the Yellow River downstream of Sanmenxia.

The project consists of a dam, flood discharging structures and power facilities. The main objectives of the project are flood control, sediment control and water supply, irrigation, and power generation. Xiaolangdi is a multi-purpose project for flood control, ice control, dredging, industrial and municipal water supply and hydroelectric power. The region surrounding the lower reaches of China's second longest river is densely populated and a major agricultural area. It has been subjected to devastating Yellow River floods, which China is determined to end. Xiaolangdi is one of 27 dams planned for the river. Yellow River projects are especially challenging because of local conditions. Rapid soil erosion upstream builds up into high sediment levels downstream. This raises the river bed and causes floods.

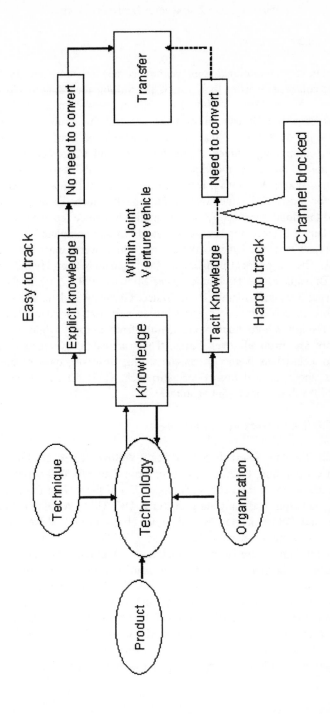

Figure 6.1 A framework for effective knowledge transfer

Major Joint Venture Companies

Three European-led international joint venture companies split the construction contracts. The contracts, worth a total of US$883 million according to World Bank estimates, were let in 1994. Yellow River Contractors formed by Impregilo, Hochtief, Italstrada and Bureau 14 won the construction contract for the river closure works, the 51.8x106 m³ main dam and associated structures. Xiaolangdi Joint-Venture, comprising Dumez, Philip Holzman and Construction Bureau 5, won work related to the underground power structures. CGIC, a joint-venture of Ed Zublin, Strabag, Wayss & Freytag, Del Favero, Salini and Bureaux 7 and 11 won the contract for intake and outlet works, the tunnels which discharge water and sediment, and the flood overflow. (Spie Batignolles has since replaced Del Favero.)

The Xiaolangdi Project was started in June 1994 and completed in September 2000. The project was divided into three Lots, which were undertaken by three joint ventures. The major local partners are the companies from Hydraulic-power Engineering Bureaux of the Hydraulic-power Ministry, P.R.C., while the foreign partners are multinationals mainly from France, Germany and Italy. There are a number of foreign sub-contractors and Chinese sub-contractors involved in the project. The foreign sub-contractors are mainly from Europe, while the Chinese sub-contractors are from all over China. Their arrival at Xiaolangdi, brought engineers and technicians from all over the world. However, most of the skilled and unskilled labour is local from Henan Province. Table 6.1 shows the relevant information of the three major joint ventures.

Statistics of Foreigners Working on Xiaolangdi

As confirmed by the International Office, Yellow River Hydraulic-power Development Corporation, P.R.C., there were more than 170, 000 people working on the construction site at the peak work, about 750 of them were foreigners from 51 countries, including Germany, France, Italy, UK, USA, Australia, Columbia, South Africa and Pakistan, etc. According to Zhang (1997), there are various patterns in terms of management style, such as: (1) Chinese – Foreign – Chinese; (2) Chinese – Foreign – Foreign; and (3) Chinese – Foreign – Foreign – Chinese. Besides the Chinese language, English is the major language of communication at the Xiaolangdi construction site. It has to be noted that language is a crucial barrier between Chinese and foreigners. Interpreters and translators were employed from the beginning to the completion of the project. It is believed that there was a grand scenario of culture diversity and philosophical sophistication among the peoples who worked on the project as they were from different countries with different cultural backgrounds, different living habits, and working experiences.

Items	Lot 1: Dam project	Lot 2: Flood discharge Engineering	Lot 3: Power generating system
Joint ventures	Yellow River Contractor (YRC)	Sino-German–Italian Joint Venture (CGIC)	Xiaolangdi Joint Venture (XJV)
Major partner and its share	Impregilo S.P.A. (Italy) 36.5%	Zublin (German) 26%	Dumez (France), 44%
Partners and their share	- Hochtief A.G. (German) 36.5% - Italstrade S.P.A. (Italy) 14% - Hydraulic-power bureau No.14 (China) 13%	- Strabag (German) 18% - Wagss & Freytag A.G. (German) 15% - Del Favero S.P.A. (Italy) 15% - Salini S.P.A. (Italy) 14% - Hydraulic-Power Bureau No.7, (China) 6% - Hydraulic-Power Bureau No. 11, (China) 6%	- Holzmann (German) 44% - Hydraulic-Power Bureau No.6 (China) 12%
Main subcontractors	- French Substructure Company - Tianjin Substructure Bureau	- TEB - OTFF - China Hydraulic-power Bureau No.1 (Liaoning) - No.3 (Shanxi) - No.4 (Qinghai) - Ministry of Railway, Bureau No.18 - Henan Yima Mining Bureau - Henan Jiaozu Mining Bureau - Shanxi Hydraulic-power Bureau	- FCB (French) - Luoyang Mining Machinery Plant - Luoyang Gold Bureau - Hydraulic-power Bureau No.4 - No.6 (Liaoning) - No.8 (Hunan) - Ministry of Railway, Bureau No.18
		- Hydraulic-power Bureau No. 11 (Henan) - RODIO (Italy)	

Table 6.1 Relevant information of the three major joint-ventures

Source of manpower	Mainly from Hydraulic-power Bureau No.14 (Yunnan, Kunming) and the unskilled labour are local	Mainly from subcontractors and the unskilled labour are local	Mainly from subcontractors and the unskilled labour are local
Manpower employed at peak of work	2400	9000	2600
Date of winning project	30-04-1994	08-06-1994	30-04-1994
Date of signing draft agreement	28-05-1994	28-06-1994	28-05-1994
Date of signing contract	16-07-1994	16-07-1994	16-07-1994
Contract volume	RMB560 million $216million	RMB 1. 9 billion	RMB316 million $84.21 million
Time for completion	91 months	84 months	74 months
Date of completion	31-12-2001	30-06-2001	31-07-2000
Date of starting work	June 1994	July 1994	June 1994

Table 6.1 (Continued)

Source: International Office, Yellow River Hydraulic-power Development Corporation

Case Study

Against the problem areas, the intention of the Case Study was to use the project to establish a systematic model for the transfer process of tacit knowledge. The Case Study that lasted for two years, identified the typical management structure of Sino-foreign joint venture in Xiaolangdi by examining the existing resources and interviewing the management staff of the project Lot 1, with which significant insight into the investigation of the dyadic interaction[1] had been approached. Furthermore, the study had established a platform for a more in-depth analysis of transfer process of management know-how between foreign and local partners, in terms of explicit and tacit knowledge transfer, dyadic interaction, channel of transfer and the influencing factors.

Aims and Objectives

The aims and objectives of the Case Study were to:

- Develop a typical management structure of Sino-foreign joint venture in Xiaolangdi for the identification of the physical structure of the dyadic interaction.
- Develop a framework of the transfer of management know-how through human interaction within a Sino-foreign joint venture project.
- Refine the framework by using Assessment Inventory survey.

The study concentrated on the more tacit forms of management knowledge, and how these could be transferred through the vehicle of joint ventures between multinational foreign contractors and the new generation of Chinese construction companies. Based upon the premises that tacit knowledge is transferred through human interaction, a basic benchmark framework for the transfer process of tacit knowledge has been developed. This Case Study was to observe the interaction of a number of dyads, comprising one foreign and one local manager. In so doing, a set of factors and the key elements influencing knowledge transfer had been explored. The results had been incorporated into the framework, which will be further developed and validated in the main study.

Assessment Inventory Survey with Interview

As has been established previously, the nature of the current research has finally resulted in the adoption of a combined methodology, where the Assessment Inventories were used as a basic element of the survey, and simultaneously the semi-structured interviews were undertaken. The purpose of deploying this

---

[1] This is not to be innovative. "Dyadic interaction" is used to interpret the "communication" and alternatively the "knowledge transfer process" between foreign and local managers.

combined methodology was to try to make data collected more accurate and practical to the present research.

The Case Study of the current research has been primarily based on the Assessment Inventory and semi-structured interview with qualitative analysis. The study also relied on direct observation (of the working environment, activities and interaction of foreign and local managers within Xiaolangdi Project) and analysis of the relevant data. The Assessment Inventories, which were designed with an identical set of statements, were delivered to the managers (both foreign and local) in the Xiaolangdi Project. The managers were expected to show their perspective and attitude towards each statement by ticking the possible answers. In each Assessment Inventory there are in total twenty questions, which cover:

- General information of Method Statement.
- Authority over Method Statement.
- Reasons of using Method Statement.
- What is transferred?
- How is knowledge transferred?
- The patterns of knowledge transfer.
- The key and critical issues in dealing with Method Statement.
- The consequences of knowledge transfer.

It was assumed that in this approach the information and data collected would be factual, quantitative and with features in common. The assessment inventories would be particularly appropriate at this stage since the aim was to quantify the relative importance of different responses to statements about a set of well-defined topics. It could also provide an overview for researchers to carry out the later interviews.

Semi-structured Interviews

Interviews with the foreign and local partners of the joint venture projects were a valuable source of primary research material and information. The semi-structured interview was adopted in the Case Study of the Xiaolangdi Project in order to explore new topics, sensitive and emotive issues based upon the Assessment Inventory.

The semi-structured interviews were constructed and focused around the central aims and objectives of current research themes. The major questions were asked as follows:

- What has been transferred between foreign and local partners during the execution of the project?
- What are the barriers in achieving successful knowledge transfer?
- How is knowledge being transferred?

- Why is knowledge transferred?
- What is the result of knowledge transfer?

The common concerns generated from the assessment inventories were also taken into consideration during the discussions with interviewees. There are both open-ended and focused questions covered in the semi-structured interviews. The initial open-ended questions were designed to encourage respondents to express their feeling and experiences when they had intimate interaction in the joint venture organisation. This phase of the interview yielded most of the new and significant insights in the study. Then, the questions followed would focus on why knowledge transfer takes place, channel of knowledge transfer, influence factors and dyadic interaction.

Problems in Conceptualising and Measuring Knowledge Transfer

In order to track the tacit knowledge transfer process, an Assessment Inventory for the present research project was designed and used during the first two study trips to Xiaolangdi when the interviews were undertaken. It was found that the key questions highlighted in the Assessment Inventory were more theoretical rather than operational on the construction site in Xiaolangdi. There was a gap between understanding academic research problems and approaching the phenomenon of knowledge transfer in the life world. Therefore, a more approachable and fundamental study was arranged in July 2000 with the John Laing Life Centre Construction Site in Newcastle upon Tyne, the UK. After this study, a multi-sectional Assessment Inventory was further developed based upon the original Assessment Inventory, with a view to approach the measurement of the process of tacit knowledge transfer particularly in dealing with the Method Statement in the construction practice. This inventory had been tested and commented in Xiaolangdi by mangers (both foreign and local) during the later trips. Further data were collected primarily by having a Knowledge Transfer Seminar, which was organised in Xiaolangdi, and attended by foreign and local managers from the three major joint-venture construction organisations and professional consultants of both the client and the World Bank. This had enabled the researcher to further develop the Assessment Inventory.

Systematic Arrangement of the Studies

During the years of 1998 and 1999, a total of six study trips to Xiaolangdi were arranged. In particular, every study was undertaken with a specific purpose of achieving aims and objectives of the research. Prior to the study, in terms of what to identify and what to finalise, appropriate preparation was made. The interviews were conducted in Chinese and English and were recorded. Table 6.2 shows the systematic arrangement of the Case Study.

	Date	Objectives	Achievements
1	29th, 30th, August 1998	Autonomy of joint venture	Typical organisation of Sino-German Joint Venture
2	19th, 20th, April 1999	Building of transfer model	Knowledge transfer model, Knowledge transfer Assessment Inventory
3	29th, 30th, July 1999	Identification	Motivation of knowledge transfer, influence factors, tacit knowledge transfer
4	28th, 29th, September, 1999	Identification	Channel of tacit knowledge transfer, success of tacit knowledge transfer
5	24th, 25th, April 2000	Identification and finalisation	Critical issues, critical operation of knowledge transfer
6	2nd, 3rd, August 2000	Method Statement	Knowledge transfer in dealing with Method Statement

Table 6.2 Systematic arrangement schedule of the Case Study

With the assistance and support of management of the Xiaolangdi project, the six study trips of the Case Study to Xiaolangdi were carried out. It was encouraging that interviews were undertaken and the aims and objectives of the study had been achieved. The interviewees whom the researcher interviewed were in fact from different countries. Most of them were from joint-venture companies, who were contractors and sub-contractors in the Xiaolangdi Project while some of them were from the client organisation. An agenda for the interviews is shown in Table 6.3.

Presentation of Case Study Data

This section will first discuss the data collection process. Then the section will present an anatomy of joint-venture projects, with the implications of the physical structure of management dyads composed of a local and foreign element. Furthermore, the section will present the findings of the Case Study and the benchmark framework of tacit knowledge transfer.

Data Collection Process and Quantitative Data

Data were collected primarily by individual interviews with the managers (foreign and local) of the relevant construction organisations. This had enabled the researcher to track the development of collaborative relationships over time.

Organisation	Nationality	Interviewee
CGIC Joint-venture Xiaolangdi Multipurpose Dam Project	German, Italian, English	3
Yellow River Contractors Xiaolangdi Multipurpose Dam Project	Italian	2
Enterprise Development Yellow River Water & Hydropower Development Corporation	Chinese	10
Construction Economics Ministry of Construction	Chinese	1
International Co-operation Division, Construction Management Department Ministry of Construction	Chinese	3
International Project Managers (Consultant to the World Bank and the Client)	Canadian	6
Total		25

Table 6.3 Interview agenda of the Case Study

Qualitative data were collected directly from interviews and observations in the field study. Quantitative data were obtained from the results of the assessment inventories.

The quantitative data presented here is in the form of a summary of the 52 copies of the assessment inventories returned to the researcher. Based on the previous study trips, fifty-two copies of the Assessment Inventory with an identical set of questions were delivered to the managers (both local and foreign) in the

Xiaolangdi Project and all the copies were returned. The assessment inventories were designed in both English and Chinese version. The English versions are for foreign partners while the Chinese are for the local partners. A summary of all the responses in the Case Study is presented.

Typical Management Structure of Sino-foreign Joint-venture

The primary interest of this research was in how tacit knowledge was transferred through human interaction. The unit of analysis would therefore be a dyad with one foreign member and the other local, and whose roles demand that they work together. Based on the interviews of foreign and local managers, a typical management structure has been established. This is important not only because it can provide better understanding of a joint venture organisation, but also because it is the first step to present an anatomy of joint venture projects, which will establish a platform to enable the researcher to have further study of the knowledge transfer process through the analysis and observation of dyadic interaction.

The following points in the typical management structure of joint venture bear significant implications for the further study of the knowledge transfer process.

- Foreign manager with Chinese assistant in each department;
- Minority foreign engineers with majority Chinese engineers in each department;
- There is no foreigner in the Safety Department.

Figure 6.2 shows the typical management structure of a Sino-foreign joint - venture in the Xiaolangdi Project, from which we can identify the physical structure of the dyadic interaction within the joint venture. An interesting point that we noticed that there is no foreign staff in the Safety Department, as it is believed that there exists the measures and requirements in terms of health and safety in construction provided by the Chinese government.

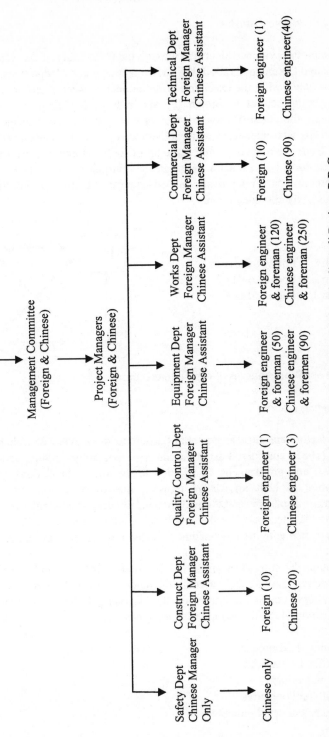

Figure 6.2 Typical management structure of Sino-foreign joint-ventures in the Xiaoliangdi Project, P.R.C.

Tacit Knowledge Transfer

The empirical evidence identified through the Case Study of the Xiaolangdi project (Lihua and Greenwood, 2000) has shown that tacit knowledge transfer occurs from time to time during the execution of the project between members of management dyads, composed of a foreign (F) and a local (L) element. The Case Study permitted the identification of the various "dyads" or management pairs of individuals who inter-react with each other as part of their managerial role. In fact these dyads are numerous, and made up of foreign-foreign (F-F), foreign-local (F-L), local-local (L-L) but for the immediate purposes of the current research, only the foreign-local (F-L) dyads are of interest. Figure 6.3 represents the work patterns of dyadic interaction.

Pattern 1   Foreign-Foreign
Pattern 2   Local-Local
Pattern 3   Foreign-Local

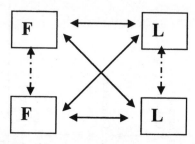

Figure 6.3 Work patterns of dyadic interaction

Influencing Factors

Many factors are cited as potential barriers to the success of technology transfer. Samli (1985) considered six dimensions – geography, culture, economy, people, business, and government. In addition to the above dimensions, contrary to the motivation of tacit knowledge transfer, one of the important barriers is the resistance of change or the unwillingness to accept knowledge transfer. It seems that there is a tendency for the elderly to be reluctant to accept knowledge transfer in accordance with the information collected through the Case Study of Xiaolangdi project.

Within the context of Hofstede (1980) and Hofstede and Bond's (1988) five dimensions of culture and based on the model of technology transfer developed by Tung (1994), the Case Study of the Xiaolangdi Project has made a further investigation of the following influencing factors:

- Cultural difference.
- Language barriers.
- Social values.
- Different objectives.
- Technical development level.

These factors will be explored and further explained in the Structured Survey, which will be incorporated into the research framework.

Motivation for Knowledge Transfer

The data collected through semi-structured interviews suggests that on the construction site in Xiaolangdi, the local partners are keen to have knowledge transferred by the foreign partners, particularly tacit knowledge such as practical management know-how, problem-solving and decision-making techniques. It is true that the transferee does not only want to absorb "know-how" but also "know-why". As a matter of fact, the transfer of know-how and skills from one group to another group is an act of power. However, the foreign partners believe that transferring management knowledge to partners is an effective approach to completing the construction project. It seems therefore that there is congruence between transferor and the transferee in the desire to see tacit knowledge being transferred.

It should be noted that under the commercial pressures of completing a project to time, quality and cost, it is not always feasible to undertake a formalised commitment to transfer. Many commentators believe that this needs to be organised and funded separately.

Mechanisms of Transferring Knowledge

The result of the Case Study of the Xiaolangdi Project suggests that the Method Statement appears to be in (a) formal form, such as well-structured written form, and (b) informal form, such as a simple note, a rough sketch, and sometimes a Method Statement can be in a verbal form, such as a message. Explicit knowledge is often transferred through well-structured written form while tacit knowledge is transferred when the message has been passed by. The foreign party normally has the final say in terms of hard construction technology in dealing with the Method Statement. However, it should be noted that 80 percent of the respondents of foreign and local managers in Xiaolangdi confirmed that knowledge transfer, in particular in terms of management know-how is a "two-way process" between multinational and local partners, while 8 percent of the respondents believe that knowledge transfer is one way from foreign to local.

What is Being Transferred?

It should be pointed out 84 percent of the respondents stated in the inventories that there is more demand of tacit knowledge transfer such as soft knowledge, management know-how than for explicit knowledge transfer such as hard knowledge, construction technology, which has been in line with the result of the previous interview. There is less demand of knowledge transfer in dealing with technical problems, such as construction technology; however, there is significant demand for knowledge transfer in dealing with administrative problems, in particular, claims and anti-claims. Local partners are eager to absorb management know-how in dealing with claims and anti-claims. Under the centralised planning economy, construction itself was regarded as construction, not a means for making profits. However, in the market economy, construction has been taken as an approach of making large profits. Therefore, claims and anti-claims have become critical issues in the whole life of a project.

A Model of Knowledge Transfer

As described in the previous section, knowledge can be divided into two components, namely explicit and tacit. Explicit knowledge and tacit knowledge have different channels of transfer, which has been developed in the Case Study in Xiaolangdi. Given the nature of both explicit knowledge and tacit knowledge, with consideration of the joint venture vehicle, a basic framework of knowledge transfer was constructed.

Figure 6.4 represents the knowledge transfer framework of both explicit knowledge and tacit knowledge, generated from the literature (Polanyi, 1967; Woherem, 1991; Tsang, 1995, 1997, 1998; McAulay, 1997; Maitland, 1999) and refined using data from the Case Study. However, it should be noted that in this presentation the flow of explicit knowledge is in a solid line while the flow of tacit knowledge is in a broken line. It should be emphasised that the transfer of explicit knowledge is easy to track, however, while transfer of tacit knowledge is hard to track. In the meantime, the certain channels that have been identified through the Case Study are believed to be arbitrary. Therefore, it is necessary to establish a systematic approach to keep the channels of tacit knowledge transfer unblocked.

Limitations of the Current Research Method

In terms of research methodological issues, so far the current study is based on the single Assessment Inventory survey of the Xiaolangdi project. There was a limitation to the interview arrangements and the spreading of the inventories due to time. The results and conceptual issues generated from the Case Study therefore need to be further tested in the Structured Survey. In addition, the validation of questions was designed in the Assessment Inventory not appropriately tested before being sent out to the interviewees, which might have caused misleading of the research focus and direction during interviews.

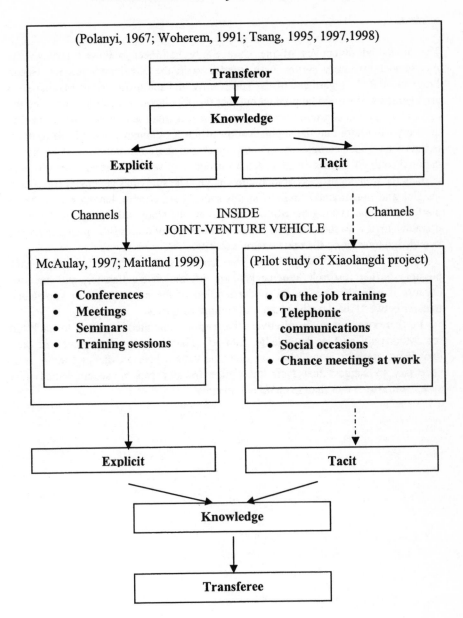

Figure 6.4 A basic framework of knowledge transfer

Summary

The aims and objectives of the Case Study had been achieved through the Assessment Inventory survey with interviews in the Xiaolangdi project, Henan Province, P.R.C., regardless of the complexity and the difficulty of making such arrangements. It should be pointed out that the Xiaolangdi project has provided the research culture background for this particular research topic. It is believed that the diversity of culture and the sophistication of the Xiaolangdi project itself (both in terms of technical complexity of the project and the construction of it by multi-national contractors) has created such a surrounding, where the researcher was able to track the transfer process of tacit knowledge. The study has generated significant insights and fundamental findings at this stage. Furthermore, having established a platform for undertaking the Structured Survey, the study will bridge the theoretic literature review in the academic world and the exploration of the phenomenon of knowledge transfer on the real construction site.

The significance of the findings from such a study is that it not only makes possible further research into mechanisms of knowledge transfer, and but also because it helps to develop the understanding of the mechanisms of knowledge transfer between the developed and developing countries.

Furthermore, this study discovers that explicit knowledge is easy to track but represents only part of knowledge transfer. Therefore, the importance of tacit knowledge transfer should be and must be established. In the meantime, it is necessary to suggest that tacit knowledge transfer can be accomplished in a systematic way rather than in an *ad hoc* manner.

Chapter 7

A Study of Jiangsu, Henan and Xinjiang

Introduction

As the title implies, this chapter briefly presents information on three regions: Jiangsu Province, Henan Province and Xinjiang Autonomous Region. These are the regions in which the Main Study - A Structured Survey was carried out. The chapter provides a number of economic indicators with particular reference to construction activity, which is believed to provide a broader context for the further understanding of the present economic status of the provinces and the region. Furthermore, the chapter focuses on a horizontal comparison of the economic indicators in these provinces and region. The chapter concludes with a summary.

Jiangsu Province, Henan Province and Xinjiang Autonomous Region

The three locations of Jiangsu Province, Henan Province and Xinjiang Autonomous Region have been selected as sample studies of construction industry in China, not because they are typical examples of the Chinese experience, but because they represent the different economies in the country. Figure 7.1 shows the geographical locations of the three regions in the People's Republic of China (P.R.C.).

A literature review shows that there is no academic work that examines the current economic development of the provinces and autonomous regions in P.R.C.. However, Table 7.1 was established based on the Construction Statistical Yearbook of China, 1998, which shows the current positions of Henan, Jiangsu and Xinjiang ranked by gross output value (GOV) of construction in the country. No doubt the construction activities in these regions will reflect the different levels of economic development in the construction industries in China as the construction industry is the pillar industry in a country's economy.

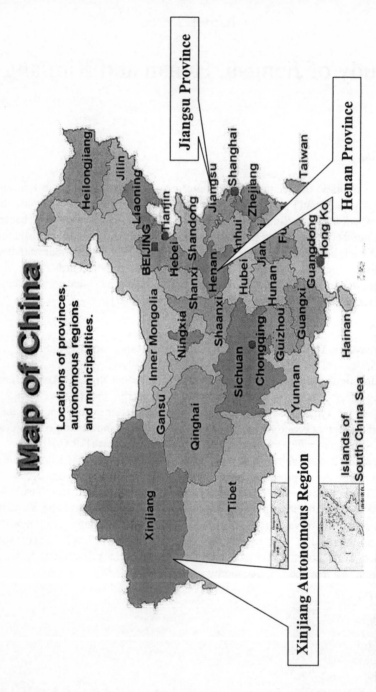

Figure 7.1 A map of China showing the locations of Jiangsu, Henan and Xinjiang

League Table of Provinces, Municipalities (directly under the Central Authorities) and Autonomous Regions in China by Gross Output Value of Construction

	Name	Capital City	GOV in RMB 1998
1	**Jiangsu**	**Nanjing**	**10,716,094**
2	Zhejiang	Hangzhou	8,773,546
3	Guangdong	Guangzhou	6,747,406
4	Shandong	Jinnan	6,479,717
5	Shanghai	Shanghai	5,524,161
6	Sichuan	Chengdu	5,206,436
7	Beijing	Beijing	5,192,363
8	Liaoning	Shenyang	4,291,256
9	Hebei	Shijiazhuang	3,760,962
10	Hubei	Wuhan	3,059,698
11	Hunan	Changsha	2,965,005
12	**Henan**	**Zhengzhou**	**2,946,903**
13	Chongqing	Chongqing	2,440,552
14	Heilonhjiang	Harbin	2,435,310
15	Anhui	Hefei	2,359,972
16	Fujian	Fuzhou	2,268,855
17	Yunnan	Kunming	2,189,844
18	Shanxi	Taiyuan	1,920,095
19	Tianjin	Tianjin	1,909,999
20	Shaanxi	Xi'an	1,642,493
21	Jilin	Changchun	1,369,882
22	Guangxi	Nanning	1,275,627
23	**Xinjiang**	**Urumqi**	**1,141,318**
24	Gansu	Lanzhou	1,056,249
25	Neimonggou	Huhhot	963,852
26	Jiangxi	Nanchang	856,436
27	Guizhou	Guiyang	767,046
28	Ningxia	Yinchuan	334,919
29	Qinghai	Xining	309,340
30	Hainan	Haikou	279,923
31	Xizhang	Lhasa	79,519

Table 7.1 The league table of provinces and regions in P.R.C.

Jiangsu Province

The economy in Jiangsu Province has grown steadily and quickly since the economic reform starting from 1978. Jiangsu, with a population of 71 million and an area of 102,600 square kilometres, is making the most of its productive location in the Yangtze River Delta. A chief economic indicator in one of China's most developed provinces, Jiangsu's GDP reached RMB335.8 billion (US$48.5 billion), a 10 percent increase over the same period of the previous year. Jiangsu is the birthplace of many of China's most important national industries. For years the value of its industrial output has ranked first in the country.

The added value of state-owned enterprises and non-public industrial enterprises with sales revenues of 5 million yuan (US$602,400) came to 102 billion yuan (US$12.3 billion), 11.7 percent more than that of the previous year. This growth was 2.3 percent above the national average. Jiangsu's export value topped US$7.7 billion in the first half of 1999. This number is an increase of 12.6 percent over the same period of the previous year. The volume of foreign trade and foreign investment for the province has surpassed one-fourth of its GDP as well as its fixed assets. By the end of 1998, there were 20,500 foreign-funded enterprises in Jiangsu, and 15,000 of them are fully operational. Foreign investments have grown to US$36 billion.

Since the economic reforms and open market policies took effect in the late 1970s, Jiangsu's economy has developed rapidly. In the past two decades, the annual growth rate was 12.8 percent. The province has also made breakthroughs in infrastructure. A modern transportation network has gradually grown across the province. The Shanghai-Nanjing Expressway, as well as the Nanjing-Lianyungang and Nanjing-Nantong grade A highways, now open to traffic, have made economic and social development easier. Two other projects, the Nanjing Lukou International Airport and the South Jiangsu section of the Beijing-Hangzhou Grand Canal, have been completed. A third transportation magnet, the Jiangyin-Yangtze River Road Bridge, is now also open to traffic. Construction on two other key projects, the Nanjing Yangtze River No 2 Bridge and the North Jiangsu Expressway, has meanwhile been accelerated.[1]

Henan Province

Located in the central and eastern part of China, at the middle and lower reaches of the Yellow River, Henan Province has an area of 167,000 square kilometres and a population of 88.61 million. It was the birthplace of the Yellow River Culture. According to a large number of popular legends and historic records, it was here that

---

[1] This is derived from the Internet page of *China International Economic Consultants Co., Ltd (CIEC) Issue date: December 28, 1999.*

Fuxi, Nuwa, Xuanyuan Huangdi, Diku, Zhuanxu, the ancestors of the Chinese nation, created Chinese civilization.

The Yellow River basin has been called the cradle of the Chinese nation where mankind lived as early as 500,000 to 600,000 years ago. In Henan Province several hundred cultural sites of the Neolithic Age (4,000 to 10,000 years ago) have been found. The famous Peiligang, Yangshao, and Longshan Cultures reflect the prosperity of this area during the late period of primitive society. From the period of 21st century B.C., when the Xia Dynasty, the first dynasty in China's history, was established, to the Northern Song Dynasty, more than 20 dynasties with more than 200 emperors set or moved their capital cities here.

Henan Province has eight high-new technology industry development zones and seven provincial economy and technology development zones, with Zhengzhou and Luoyang being the country's high-new technology industry development zones. There are two first-class airports (Zhengzhou and Luoyang), one first-class railway port (Zhengzhou East Railway Station), three second-class highway ports (Zhengzhou, Luoyang and Shangqiu) in Henan. Taking 1998 as an example, the whole province maked use of about US$ 1.034 billion foreign investment.

Henan Province has opened more sectors to foreign investors. In addition to the technology industry, the province has opened to overseas investors the agricultural industry, the stockbreeding industry, the transportation industry, the service industry, the retail industry, education, the pharmaceutical industry, land exploitation and so on. Currently, investors from more than 60 countries, including Japan, the United States, Germany, Britain and Singapore, have come to Henan to develop their business. In total, there are more than 2000 joint ventures in Henan. The province has 101 cities and towns open[2] to foreigners, with almost every city or town having at least one joint venture.   Henan has established co-operation and science-technology communication with more than 30 countries and districts. It also has made long term and relatively stable science-technology co-operation with some research institutes in Japan, the United States, Germany, Britain and so on. In 1998, Henan's total turnover reached US$69.94 million,   an increase of 7.6 percent compared with the previous year.[3]

Xinjiang Autonomous Region

Xinjiang is the shortened name of Xinjiang Uygur Autonomous Region. Xinjiang has a population of 17.18 million. Situated in Northwest China and in the centre of the Eurasian continent, it is over 1,600,000 square kilometres in area, making up

---

[2] This means a city where infrastructure and investment surrounding have been well established to accommodate foreign investors.

[3] This is derived from Internet page of *The People's Government of Henan Province, P.R.C. China, China Council for the Promotion of International Trade, Henan Multimedia Information Bureau, Henan Info. Port, 2000.*

one-sixth of the entire territory of China, the biggest of all the country's provinces and autonomous regions.

Xinjiang's economy presents a good situation of "high increase and low inflation". There are bumper harvests in agriculture and rapid increases in industrial production. Investment, consumption and exports have maintained a certain degree of increase. The financial and monetary situation is regular. But at the same time, with economic development, there appear problems that cannot be ignored. The basis for further economic development is not stable yet; the pace of structural adjustment is still slow; the production management of state-owned enterprises is difficult; and the overall situation of the economy is still not ideal.

As a major region in the development of west China, Xinjiang is abundant in exploitable resources and has great potential for developing the feature economy and forming new economic growth points. Xinjiang, also rich in mineral resources, plans to construct China's biggest petroleum and natural gas industrial base and an important petrochemical industrial base in west China in the coming five years. Meanwhile, it will finish constructing a textile production base, a non-ferrous metals industrial base and other industrial bases.

Infrastructure construction, focused on transportation and water conservancy, will also be a key local industry requiring major input in the next five years. The Xinjiang government plans to invest 70 billion yuan in infrastructure construction, 23 billion yuan of which will be directed into highway construction and renovation. Besides, it will speed up the construction of China-Kirghizia-Uzbekistan Railway, improve the infrastructure of Urumqi and Kashi airports, and quicken the construction of communication information network. Xinjiang neighbours Gansu Province and Qinghai Province to the Southeast and Tibet in the South; and borders eight countries in all other directions, that is, Mongolia to the Northeast, Russia, Kazakhstan, Kyrgyzstan and Tajikistan to the Northwest and Afghanistan, Pakistan and India to the Southwest. The region has a national boundary of over 5,000 kilometres, longer than that of any other of the country's provinces and regions. The situation endows Xinjiang with a natural geographical advantage for its reform and opening to the outside world.

Xinjiang is surrounded by mountains. It depends upon snow-melt water from these mountains to irrigate its oases. Xinjiang's oases are isolated, separated from each other by large expanses of desert. Transportation is poor and expensive; as a result many regions are basically closed economies. In 1992, the average income of people in the Hotan region was RMB903 per year and RMB1185 in Kashgar, respectively the lowest and third lowest per capita income of Xinjiang's regions.

From 1949, ethnic Han emigration to Xinjiang rose and fell with events in eastern China. The great majority of the emigrants to Xinjiang in 1990 [88 percent] came from rural China but were, in general, better educated than the average Xinjiang resident. Xinjiang will pay more attention to ecological and environmental construction and attach equal importance to environmental protection and pollution control.

Economic Indicators in the Construction Industry

As has been established previously, this study sets its boundary within the context of the construction industry in China. It should be noted that it is hard to obtain the up-to-date data of economic development in a changing environment, in particular with construction sector in the fast and ever-changing economy of China.

In order to identify the different levels of construction industry among Jiangsu, Henan and Xinjiang, a certain number of economic indicators have been chosen from the Year Book of 1998, which was compiled by the Department of Statistics on Investment in Fixed Assets of the State Statistical Bureau, published by China Statistical Publishing House, presented in Table 7.2.

The intention is to have a comparative study between the main economic indicators in construction and the economic indicators of foreign funded economic units in the three regions. Therefore, two sets of economic indicators have been chosen. One set concerns main economic indicators of the whole industry of the three regions, such as the following:

- Gross output value of construction.
- Number of projects.
- Construction quality projects.
- Statistics on machinery and equipment.
- Value added of construction.
- Total floor space completed.
- Total capital and structure of total assets.
- Liabilities and creditors' equity.
- Total profit.
- Total number of construction enterprises.

The other set concerns economic indicators of construction enterprises of foreign founded economic units, which includes foreign funded economic units, economic units funded by entrepreneurs from Hong Kong, Macao and Taiwan, and units of other types of ownership. These indicators are as follows:

- Gross output value of construction.
- Number of projects.
- Construction quality projects.
- Statistics on machinery and equipment.
- Value added of construction.
- Total floor space completed.
- Total capital and structure of total assets.
- Liabilities and creditors' equity.
- Total profit.
- Total number of construction enterprises.

	Jiangsu	Henan	Xinjiang	National Total	Remarks
1. Gross output value of construction (10000 yuan)	10,716,094	2,946,903	1,141,318	91,264,777	10,000 yuan
2. Number of projects (projects)	63,888	29,714	11,877	678,767	Project
3. Construction quality projects (projects)	14,578	6,593	1,695	131,337	Project
4. Statistics on machinery and equipment (pieces)	560,987	244,518	64,252	5,604,603	Piece
5. Value added of construction (10000 yuan)	2,620,881	795,700	345,229	25,405,426	10,000 yuan
6. Total floor space completed (10000 sqare metre)	15,750.6	4,984.4	1,400.3	128,680.3	10,000 square metre
7. Total capital and structure of total assets (10000 yuan)	1,979,955	583,130	309,044	22,316,538	10,000 yuan
8. Liabilities and creditors' equity (10000 yuan)	8,241,901	1,906,875	1,018,007	79,137,411	10,000 yuan
9. Total profit (10000 yuan)	113,507	26,029	-4,347	1099,170	10,000 yuan
10. Total number of construction enterprises (companies)	3,195	1,975	650	44,107	Company

Table 7.2 Main economic indicators of construction in Jiangsu, Henan and Xinjiang, P.R.C.

Construction Enterprises of Foreign Funded Economic Units	Jiangsu	Henan	Xinjiang	National Total	Remarks
1. Gross output value of construction (10000 yuan)	95,065	10,343	0	704,912	10,000 yuan
2. Number of projects (projects)	853	97	0	4,539	Project
3. Construction quality of project (projects)	156	37	0	637	Project
4. Statistics on machinery and equipment (pieces)	2,936	329	0	29,228	Piece
5. Value added of construction (10000 yuan)	21,281	3,248	0	163,739	10,000 yuan
6. Total floor space completed (10000 square metre)	37.5	0.9	0	196.8	10,000 square metre
7. Total capital and structure of total assets (10000 yuan)	19,384	3,049	0	259,947	10,000 yuan
8. Liabilities and creditors' equity (10000 yuan)	61,114	9,864	0	548,588	10,000 yuan
9. Total profits (10000 yuan)	4,031	251	0	32,212	10,000 yuan
10. Total Number of foreign funded economic units (companies)	37	11	0	454	Company

Table 7.2 (Continued)

Note 1:This category of construction enterprises includes foreign funded economic units, economic units funded by entrepreneurs from Hong Kong, Macao, and Taiwan, and units of other types of ownership

Table 7.2 shows the various economic indicators of construction industry in Jiangsu Province, Henan Province and Xinjiang Autonomous Region.

Comparison among the Three Regions

It is not intended to present any particular mathematical relationship or models by presenting the following bar charts. All the bar charts are mere visual aids showing the main features of the construction industry among these regions. This is to allow for a horizontal comparison of the various economic indicators of construction industry among Jiangsu Province, Henan Province and Xinjiang Autonomous Region in the Peoples' Republic of China. Figure 7.2–7.20 present the comparison of the economic indicators among Jiangsu Province, Henan Province and Xinjiang Autonomous Region.

Main Economic Indicators in Construction

Figures 7.2–7.11 show the mere comparison of main economic indicators in construction industry in Jiangsu Province, Henan Province and Xinjiang Autonomous Region, Peoples' Republic of China.

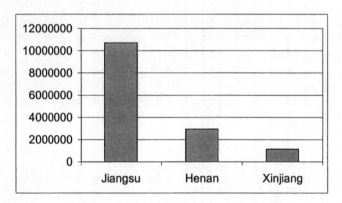

Figure 7.2 Gross output value of construction

Figure 7.2 shows a comparison of the gross output value (GOV) of construction among the three regions. GOV is the total value of construction products shown in terms of currency that were completed by the construction enterprises up to date. It is an important indicator to reflect production scale and the development speed of construction industry, which is an important base to calculate the economic results, labour productivity and the proportion of construction industry in the national economy.

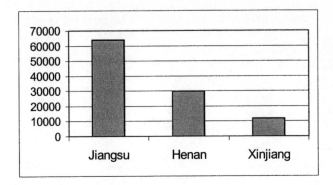

Figure 7.3 Number of projects

Figure 7.3 shows a comparison of the number of construction projects among the three regions. The number of projects means the total number of construction projects completed by the construction enterprises in the regions so far.

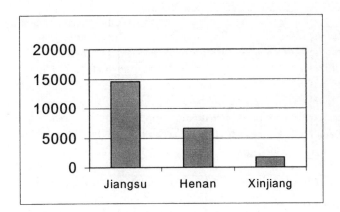

Figure 7.4 Construction quality projects

Figure 7.4 shows a comparison of construction quality projects among the three regions. The construction quality project means construction projects completed with high quality. Most construction items in the projects were completed in accordance with the required standard set by the government. This is often assessed and examined by construction experts.

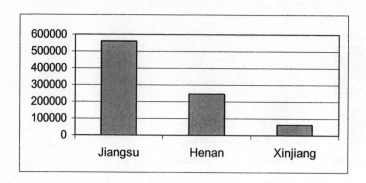

Figure 7.5 Statistics on machinery and equipment

Figure 7.5 shows a comparison of the statistics on machinery and equipment among the three regions. These figures represent the quantity of construction machinery and equipment possessed by the construction enterprises in the regions.

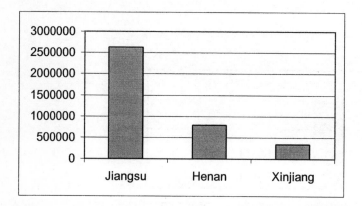

Figure 7.6 Value added construction

Figure 7.6 shows a comparison of value-added construction among the three regions. Value-added construction means the final economic result in terms of the currency of production and the operation of the construction industry to date.

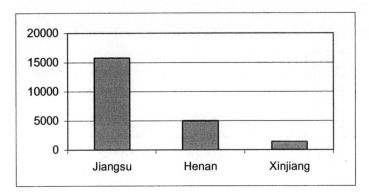

Figure 7.7 Total floor space completed

Figure 7.7 shows a comparison of total floor space completed so far among the three regions. These figures show the total construction areas completed in accordance with the requirement of architectural design and put into utilisation.

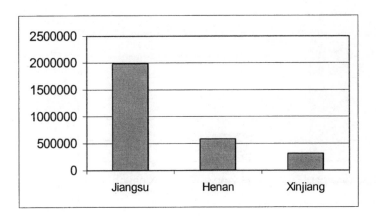

Figure 7.8 Total capital and structure of total assets

Figure 7.8 shows a comparison of total capital and structure of total assets among the three regions. This represents the economic resources in terms of currency that enterprises possess and are able to control, which includes operational assets, long term investment, fixed assets, special items, invisible assets and other assets.

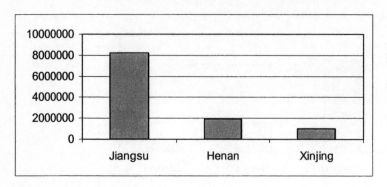

Figure 7.9 Liabilities and creditors' equity

Figure 7.9 shows a comparison of liabilities and creditors' equity in construction industry among the three regions. This means the liabilities and creditors' equity that the enterprises would pay in terms of capital or manpower. It should be pointed that this indicator still bears features of the command economy.

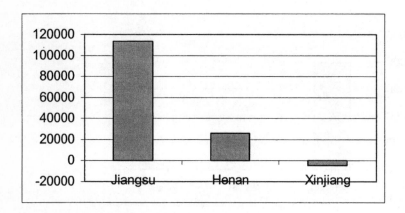

Figure 7.10 Total profit (10000 yuan)

Figure 7.10 shows a comparison of the total profit of the construction industry among the three regions. It should be noted that the construction industry in Xinjiang makes a loss.

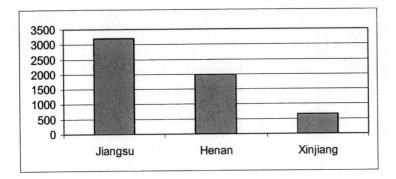

Figure 7.11 Total number of construction enterprises

Figure 7.11 shows the comparison of the total number of construction enterprises among the three regions. In fact, there is a strict classification of construction enterprises in accordance with the Regulation No. 666 (1995) promulgated by the Ministry of Construction, P.R.C.. All the enterprises were classified as first class, second class, third class and fourth class in accordance with the human resource quality, management level, amount of capital, the ability to contract construction projects, technological capacity, and the construction performance.

Main Economic Indicators in Construction Enterprises of Foreign Funded Economic Units

In order to avoid the repetition of the previous section as they have similar implications in that the first set of main economic indicators, apart from the fact that these indicators are related to the foreign funded economic units, the second set of economic indicators of construction enterprises of foreign funded economic units will not be dwelt upon. It should be noticed that there was no record of joint ventures till 1998 in Xinjiang. Therefore, nothing is shown in all the charts of foreign funded economic units in Xinjiang.

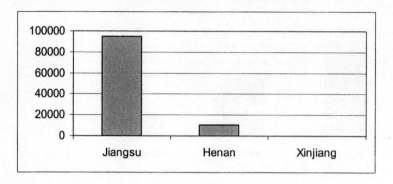

Figure 7.12 Gross output value of construction of foreign funded economic units

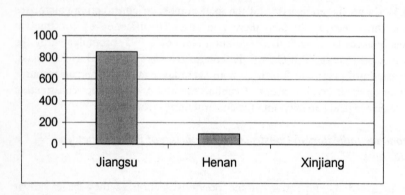

Figure 7.13 Number of projects of foreign funded economic units

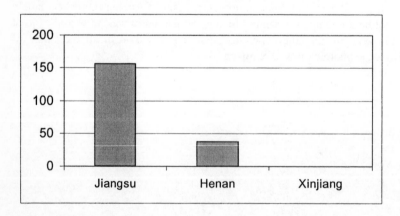

Figure 7.14 Construction quality project of foreign funded economic units

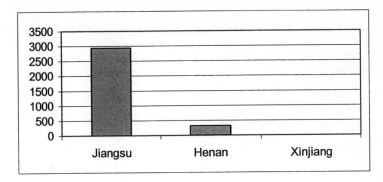

Figure 7.15 Statistics on machinery and equipment of foreign funded economic units

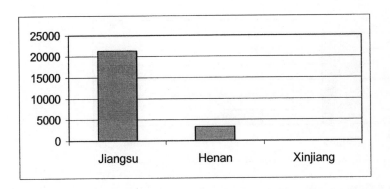

Figure 7.16 Value added of construction of foreign funded economic units

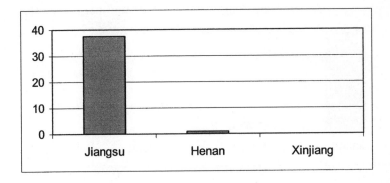

Figure 7.17 Total floor space completed by foreign funded economic units

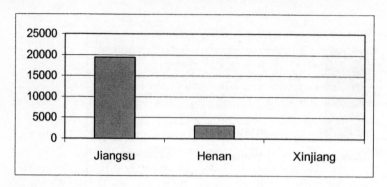

Figure 7.18 Total capital and structure of total assets of foreign funded economic units

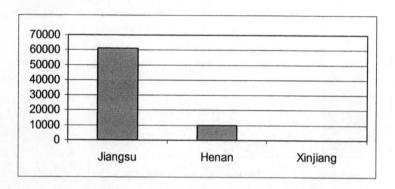

Figure 7.19 Liabilities and creditors' equity of foreign funded economic units

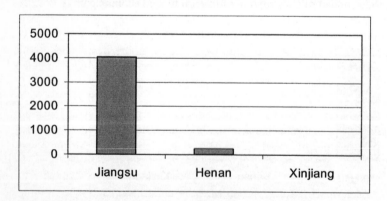

Figure 7.20 Total profits of foreign funded economic units

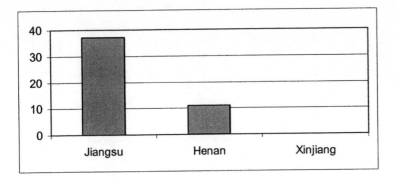

Figure 7.21 Total number of foreign funded economic units

Summary

Given the background of Jiangsu Province, Henan Province and Xinjiang Autonomous Region, based on the comprehensive comparison of the economic indicators of the construction industry in these regions, the conclusion will be that these economic indicators in these regions mirror clearly their different economic development levels in construction activity. Jiangsu Province is well-developed, Henan Province is newly-developed and Xinjing Autonomous Region is less-developed. In addition, Jiangsu Province has a strong industrial background, Henan Province has a long history and a splendid culture, with a vigorous dynamics to catch up with the coastal regions, while Xinjiang Autonomous Region benefits from immigrants from other parts of China with a large potential to develop its economy. In the next chapter, the discussion will focus on the synthesis and analysis of the implication of these economic indicators and how they give impact on the process of knowledge transfer during the operation of international joint-venture projects.

Chapter 8

A Structured Survey in Three Different Economies

Introduction

Following an examination of the background and the reasons why Jiangsu Province, Henan Province and the Xinjiang Autonomous Region were selected to be the sampling locations where the Structured Survey was undertaken, the chapter explains the aims and objectives of the Structured Survey. The chapter also addresses the issues of design rational and the main themes of Assessment Inventory, and clarifies the difference between respondents and respondents rates. However, the view that the Method Statement is an important component to approach the tracking of the knowledge transfer process is explained. Furthermore, the chapter presents the results of the Structured Survey.

The Structured Survey in Jiangsu, Henan and Xinjiang

As was established earlier, the purpose of the Structured Survey in the different economies is to further investigate and validate the research results generated from the Case Study in Xiaolangdi. It is believed that the Structured Survey, which was undertaken in a much wider context of Jiangsu Province, Henan Province and the Xinjiang Autonomous Region, will provide practical and fundamental indications of external validity.

As a matter of fact, the primary interest of the Structured Survey was to use the information collected through interviews from the Case Study and refine it. The results were then used to develop and establish the research understanding. In the Structured Survey, copies of a refined Assessment Inventory were delivered by the researcher personally and distributed by the construction authorities in the three chosen regions, Jiangsu Province, Henan Province and the Xinjiang Autonomous Region. These three locations have been chosen because they represent different economic development levels of the construction industry in China (refer to Chapter 7). Jiangsu Province, one of the coastal and advanced provinces, has a relatively well developed construction industry while the Xinjiang Autonomous Region, located in the west part of China, has an industry which is much less advanced. Henan Province, an inland province, located in the central part of China, is in the intermediate position, as was presented in Chapter 7. An appropriate consideration of these factors will contribute to the understanding of the data collected and the information obtained.

Aims and Objectives

The aims and objectives of the Structured Survey are to:

- Further define the process of knowledge transfer, with the establishment of the concept of tacit knowledge transfer identified during the Case Study;
- Refine the understanding of the process of tacit knowledge transfer based on the premises identified during the Case Study;
- Explore the relationship between knowledge transfer and economic development;
- Explore the relationship between explicit knowledge transfer and tacit knowledge transfer.

The study focuses on how knowledge (in particular tacit knowledge) was transferred between foreign and local managers when they completed a construction task - the Method Statement. It is believed that the transfer of knowledge when dealing with Method Statements will mirror the process of problem-solving and decision-making as well as the process of knowledge transfer in the whole industry.

Design Rational and the Main Themes of the Assessment Inventory

The design of the Assessment Inventory for the Structured Survey was based on the Case Study of the Xiaolangdi Project, in Henan Province, P.R.C. As has been established earlier, the focus of the Structured Survey was to identify the process of knowledge transfer through the intimate human interaction between foreign and local managers in an international joint-venture organisation when they deal with the preparation and the implementation of Method Statements. The objective of the study was to obtain practical and useful quantitative and qualitative data through the survey. Against this background, with a consideration of pattern-matching and explanation-building when undertaking quantitative analysis, a re-design of the Assessment Inventory of the Structured Survey was carried out with the following main themes being highlighted:

	Main Themes	Questions that reflect the Main Themes
1	Why a Method Statement is needed	Question 1 tries to explore various reasons why a Method Statement is needed.
2	Form of Method Statement	Question 2 tries to identify the form of a Method Statement.
3	Background to a Method Statement	Question 3 tries to identify the background knowledge of a Method Statement.
4	Further reasons for using a Method Statement	Question 4 tries to identify further reasons for using a Method Statement.
5	Authority over a Method Statement	Question 5 tries to identify which party has the authority to control a Method Statement while Question 6 tries to identify the people who are mainly involved in the process of discussing a Method Statement.
6	What knowledge is being transferred	Question 7 and 9 try to identify what knowledge is needed between foreign and local managers in terms of construction technology (hard knowledge or explicit knowledge) and management know-how (or soft knowledge or tacit knowledge), whereas Question 8 and 10 try to identify what knowledge was actually transferred in terms of hard knowledge and soft knowledge.
7	How knowledge transfer takes place	Question 11 and 12 try to identify the different channels of explicit and tacit knowledge transfer while Question 13 tries to identify the pattern of knowledge transfer.
8	Success of knowledge transfer	Question 14 tries to identify the factors which influence knowledge transfer, while Question 15 and Question 16 try to identify the factors in achieving a successful knowledge transfer and the motivators of knowledge transfer.
9	Critical and key issues	Question 17 tries to identify the critical and key issues of knowledge transfer in the process of construction.
10	Consequence of knowledge transfer	Question 18, 19 and 20 try to identify the consequence of knowledge transfer.

Table 8.1 Main themes of the Assessment Inventory

The Survey Data

The results presented in this chapter are a summary of 450 copies of the Assessment Inventory, which were returned to the researcher by the respondents from Jiangsu Province, Henan Province and the Xinjiang Autonomous Region, P.R.C. The Assessment Inventory was designed both in English and Chinese. English versions were delivered to foreigners while Chinese versions were delivered to local managers with the assistance of the construction authorities in the three regions. Appendix 6 presents a summary of the receipts of the Structured Survey from the Jiangsu Province, Henan Province and the Xinjiang Autonomous region.

Respondents

With the help and support of the Construction Management Bureaux of Jiangsu Province, Henan Province and the Xinjiang Autonomous Region, P.R.C., the copies of assessment inventories were distributed among international joint-venture companies and construction enterprises in the three regions in China. There were 450 respondents from the three regions. These respondents were key personnel from within Sino-foreign joint-venture companies and large-middle sized construction enterprises. They are departmental managers and engineers of the companies. Some respondents were the decision-makers of the enterprises, such as presidents, general managers, deputy general managers, chief engineers, and chief economists of joint-venture companies and construction enterprises. It should be noted that consultants to the World Bank and to the Chinese Government who are working at the Xiaolangdi project are also among the respondents. Table 8.2 shows the location and the whole sample of respondents in the Structured Survey.

Regions in P.R.C.	Chinese respondents	Foreign respondents	Total in Regions	Total in survey 450
Xiaolangdi	52	9	61	61
Jiangsu Province	161	-[1]	161	161
Henan Province	128	-	128	128
Xinjiang Autonomous Region	100	-	100	100

Table 8.2 Location and whole sample of the respondents in the Structured Survey

---

[1] It has been confirmed by the construction authority of the three regions that there were efforts made to involve both foreign and local managers. However, it appears that there are no foreign respondents.

Response Rate

A number of corresponding factors were carefully considered in order to have accurate answers from the respondents when designing the assessment inventories. Some key words, such as, *main, mainly, principal, primary* were highlighted in the assessment inventories. However, many respondents chose more than one answer to each question in the assessment inventories, which accounts for the different number of the total copies of assessment inventories received and the number of total responses.

Interpretation of the Structured Survey Findings

There are 20 questions in total in the assessment inventories, which are all related with the process of knowledge transfer between foreign and local partners when dealing with the Method Statement. The interpretation adopts the approach that the analysis follows in order and advances step by step. The summary of data collected from the three regions is explained by presenting pie charts and followed by a discussion with various implications for knowledge transfer being highlighted.

In accordance with the sequences and natures of the questions, given the analytical strategy of pattern-matching and explanation-building, ten major themes together with the implication for knowledge transfer are presented as follows:

Why is the Method Statement Needed?

In the survey, this theme is a starting point, left with an open answer, which is used to collect various opinions towards using a Method Statement. It should be noted that almost all of the respondents in the three regions returned the assessment inventories without answering this question. Fortunately the majority of the respondents in the Xiaolangdi Project answered this question. Of the 61 respondents 45 percent returned the assessment inventories without answer. However, Of the 61 respondents who replied with answers some even wrote a paragraph to express the reasons why the construction Method Statement was needed. The analysis suggests that there are two categories of answers. One category is functional (F), the other is administrative (A). Table 8.3 shows the briefing record of various key reasons that the respondents provided, which have been categorised as "F" and "A".

Question: why did you need to determine the Method Statement?	Functional	Administrative
Key Answers:		
"Method Statement is important to guarantee quality, time and cost of the project".	F	
"This is in accordance with requirement of the contract".		A
"This is in accordance with ISO9001"		A
"Method Statement is very effective".	F	
"Method Statement is needed for the resource allocation"	F	
"This is for the satisfaction of the client"		A
"For health and safety"		A
"It helps to solve construction problem"	F	
"For the administration of the contract"		A
Please note that the following answers are provided by respondents who gave their titles and positions as they are recorded		
"Nothing cannot be done properly without Method Statement". – A Senior Engineer and PhD candidate	F	
"Using Method Statement can clarify aims and responsibilities of both parties so that the task can be completed with high quality". – A Senior Engineer	F	
"Method Statement is the best way to solve various problems, improve productivity and make up the shortcomings of the original plan."- Project Manager	F	
"Method Statement is a way to shorten the time of completion, to guarantee the quality and improve logistic management". – An Engineer		A
"The speciality of project investment requires the use of Method Statement ". – An Engineer	F	
"Method Statement is an effective way to combine technology and management". – An Engineer	F	
"Method Statement agrees with natural law". – An Engineer	F	
"To ensure that the work is carried out orderly, efficiently and safely". – Head	F	

Consultant, Adviser and Engineer of WB		
"To organise a repetitive task in a consistent manner". – A Planning Adviser	F	
"Using Method Statement is mandatory". – A Project Service Engineer		A
"To satisfy the contractual requirements and in order to carry out the work". – Manager of Hydro-Mechanical Department	F	
"Method Statement is one of the most important document of the construction, which has a big influence on quality, organisation and cost". – Manager of Work Department		A

Table 8.3 Key answers to question 1 in the Assessment Inventory

Form of the Method Statement

As regards to the form of the Method Statement, three choices in the Assessment Inventory were provided. They are "formal document", "sketch or note" and "verbal". Among the total of 450 responses, 55.81 percent confirmed that "formal documents" were used to communicate the Method Statement. "Sketch or note" and "verbal" accounted for 31.89 percent and 12.30 percent respectively. This result implies that construction people prefer "formal document" rather than the informal means of communication. Figure 8.1 represents these different respects.

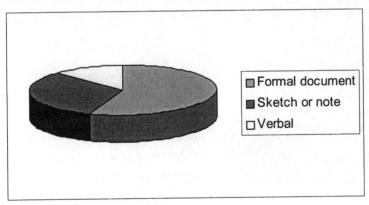

Figure 8.1 Form of the Method Statement

Foundation of the Method Statement

In terms of the foundation of the Method Statement, 53.37 percent of individuals in the study responded that the form of Method Statement was mainly based upon "contract document" while "copy of handbook" accounts for 16.59 percent, "previous MS" accounts for 18.27 percent and "handmade on spot" accounts for 11.54 percent respectively. This result implies that construction people believe that the Method Statement should be an integral part of the contract document.

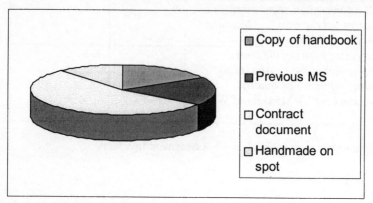

Figure 8.2 Foundation of the Method Statement

Further Reasons of Using Method Statement

It is interesting that the respondents in the three regions hold different views regarding the further reasons for using the Method Statement. "Complicated task" accounts for 9.62 percent, "resource allocation" accounts for 37.36 percent, "guidance of work" accounts for 17.90 percent and "required by client" accounts for 35.12 percent respectively. Figure 8.3 shows the different views about this issue.

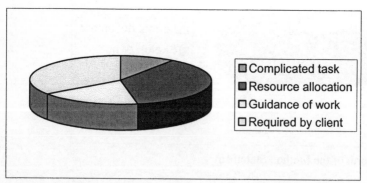

Figure 8.3 Further reasons for using the Method Statement

Authority over the Method Statement

In terms of which party has control over the Method Statement issue, 59.21 percent of the responses confirmed that the foreign and local partners should work "together" closely and make decision "together" whereas 18.34 percent of the responses still favour "local" partner and 22.34 percent of the responses still favour "foreign" partner.

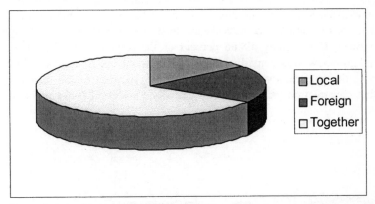

Figure 8.4 Authority over the Method Statement

Parties Involved with the Method Statement

It seems necessary for both the foreign and local partners to always discuss Method Statements together and solve the problems together. In the study, 67.61 percent of the responses confirmed the issue whereas 14.35 percent of the responses still favoured "local" partner and 16.74 percent of the responses still favoured "foreign" partner.

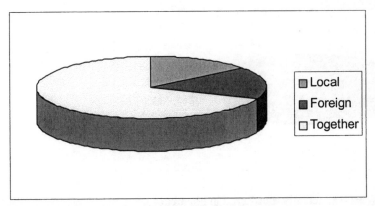

Figure 8.5 Parties involved with the Method Statement

What Is Being Transferred

The empirical evidence from the interviews carried out on the Xiaolangdi Project has shown that tacit knowledge transfer occurs from time to time during the execution of the project between members of management pairs composed of a foreign (F) and a local (L) manager. The data collected in the Structured Survey has further confirmed the transfer of tacit knowledge, (management know-how). In the survey, 80.28 percent of the responses confirmed that management know-how needed to be transferred in construction, whereas 19.72 percent of the responses confirmed that construction technology needed to be transferred between foreign and local partners. In the study, 68.66 percent of the responses confirmed that management know-how was actually transferred between the foreign and local partners during the construction practice whereas 31.11percent of the responses confirmed that construction technology was actually transferred (refer to Figure 8.7).

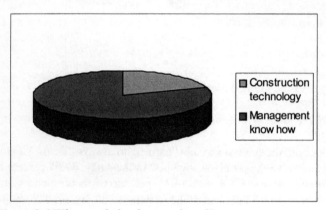

Figure 8.6 What needed to be transferred?

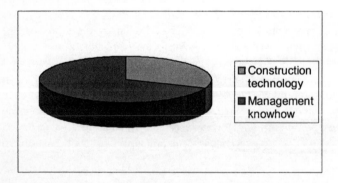

Figure 8.7 What was actually transferred in practice?

Explicit Knowledge or Tacit Knowledge

It should be noted that this theme is similar to the last theme. The repetition was used as a check on the respondents' understanding. It was apparent that the respondents had no clear understanding of "explicit" knowledge and "tacit" knowledge.

In the main study, 53.18 percent of responses confirmed that tacit knowledge needed to be transferred between foreign and local partners during the construction practice whereas 53.99 percent of the responses confirmed that it was tacit knowledge that was actually transferred. Figure 8.8 shows that tacit knowledge transfer dominates the question "what needed to be transferred" while Figure 8.9 shows that tacit knowledge transfer again dominated the question "what actually did transfer".

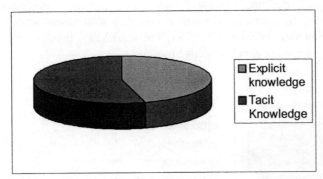

Figure 8.8 What needed to be transferred?

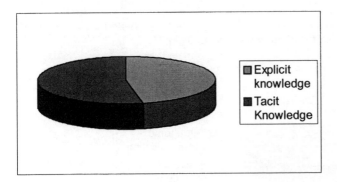

Figure 8.9 What actually did transfer?

How Was Knowledge Transferred?

The study has shown that explicit knowledge is in general transferred through formal means, such as conferences, meetings, seminars and training sessions while tacit knowledge is transferred through informal means, such as on the job training, telephonic communication, social occasions and chance meetings. In the design of the Assessment Inventory, the intention was to know the main channels for both the explicit and tacit transfer, but it seems that there is no clear trend to distinguish which channel is the main channel. "Conferences" accounts for 29.95 percent, "meetings" accounts for 33.33 percent, "seminars" accounts for 27.54 percent and "training sessions" account for 10.39 percent. "job training" account for 24.44 percent, "telephonic communication" account for 20.49 percent, "social occasions" account for 35.80 percent and "chance meetings" account for 18.17 percent. However, the study confirmed that the transfer of explicit and tacit knowledge takes place in a different environment, where they have their own special ways of transfer. Figure 8.10 shows the channels of explicit knowledge transfer while Figure 8.11shows the channel of tacit knowledge transfer.

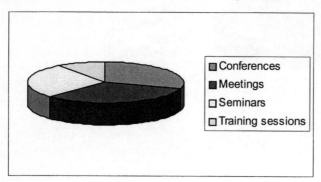

Figure 8.10 Channels of explicit knowledge transfer

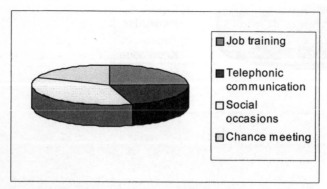

Figure 8.11 Channels of tacit knowledge transfer

Given the dimension and channels for knowledge transfer, the study discovers that explicit knowledge is often transferred through well-structured written document while tacit knowledge is transferred when the message is passed on. However, it should be noted that 51.32 percent of the responses of foreign and local managers confirmed that knowledge transfer in particular in terms of management know-how is a "two-way process" between multinational and local partners, while 33.48percent of the responses believe that knowledge transfer is one way from foreign to local and while 15.20 percent of the responses believe that knowledge transfer is one way from local to foreign. Figure 8.12 shows that "a two-way process of knowledge transfer" dominates the process of knowledge transfer.

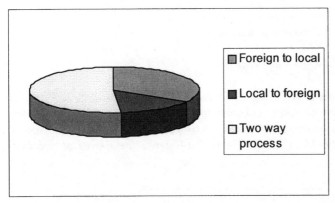

Figure 8.12 Patterns of knowledge transfer

Factors in Achieving Successful Knowledge Transfer

Barriers of Knowledge Transfer   In the survey of the literature of technology transfer, many factors, such as economy, people, business, and government, are cited as potential barriers to the success of technology transfer. In addition to the above dimension, the other factors that have been identified such as "culture", "language", "common objective" and "social value" have a significant impact on the process of knowledge transfer. However, "culture" accounts for 18.31 percent, "language" accounts for 40.85 percent, "common objective" accounts for 21.36 percent and "social value" accounts for 19.48 percent. Figure 8.13 shows the barriers to knowledge transfer.

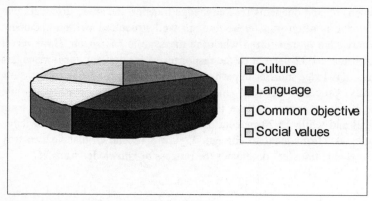

Figure 8.13 Barriers to knowledge transfer

Factors of Successful Knowledge Transfer

In terms of the factors in achieving a successful knowledge transfer, 28.87 percent Of the respondents have chosen "mutual respect", 54.46 percent of the respondents have chosen "close co-operation" while 16.67 percent have chosen "appropriate co-ordination" in the Main Study. Figure 8.14 shows the factors of successful knowledge transfer.

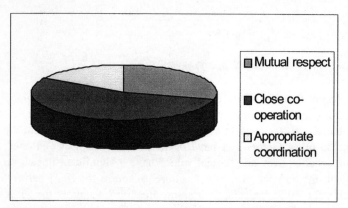

Figure 8.14 Factors of successful knowledge transfer

Motivators of Successful Knowledge Transfer In terms of the motivators in achieving a successful knowledge transfer in the study, 37.94 percent of the respondents have chosen "mutual benefit", 34.43 percent of the respondents have chosen "collaborative attitude" while 27.63 percent of the respondents have chosen "completion of task" in the Main Study. Figure 8.15 shows the motivators of successful knowledge transfer.

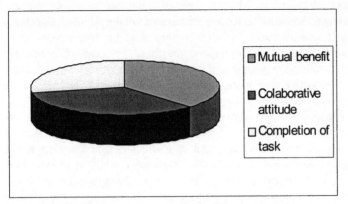

Figure 8.15 Motivators of successful knowledge transfer

Key and Critical Issues

In construction, time, cost, safety and quality are always important issues. However, the data from the Structured Survey show that people pay more attention to quality and safety issues rather than time and cost issues. "Safety" accounts for 31.43 percent and "quality" accounts for 40.63 percent while "Time" accounts for 9.21 percent and "cost" accounts for 21.90 percent. Figure 8.16 shows the different implications of the respondents' attitude towards this issue.

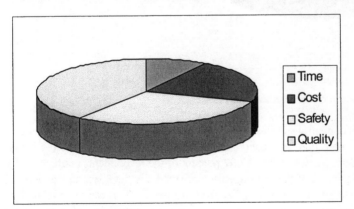

Figure 8.16 Key and critical issues

Consequence of Knowledge Transfer

During the whole life of a project contract, there are various problems. However, some of them are technical, some of them are concerned with personnel, some of them are easy to solve, some of them are not. Nevertheless, the discussion of a Method Statement is one of the ways to resolve various problems in order to make a successful project. In the study, 74.29 percent of responses confirmed that the Method Statement was "revised" after the discussion of the Method Statement between foreign and local partners while 16.26 percent of the respondents chose "implemented" and 9.45 percent of the respondents chose "rejected". This strongly indicates that the construction people are willing to exchange ideas and share information so as to improve their work. Against this background, it is possible to argue that this revised or refined Method Statement will contain significant elements of knowledge that has flowed between the two parties during the conversation, argument, and exchange of idea and information. From this study it is reasonable to suggest that knowledge, and in particular, tacit knowledge was transferred during the discussion of the Method Statement, which is in this study referred to that "tacit knowledge transfer was achieved through intimate human interaction". Figure 8.17 shows that the result of a discussion of the Method Statement leads to revision of it.

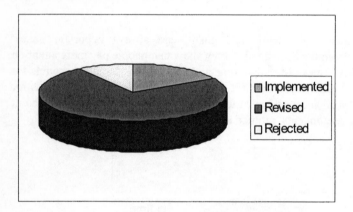

Figure 8.17 Revision of the Method Statement

If this Method Statement was revised or rejected, 59.47 percent of the responses in the study confirmed that the actual Method Statement was devised through compromise by both parties, while 12.92 percent of the respondents confirmed "by the local", 16.48 percent of the respondents confirmed "by the foreigner" and 10.47 percent of the respondents confirmed "by the third party". This seems to reconfirm the previous findings that mutual benefit, close co-operation and appropriate coordination are the important factors in achieving a successful knowledge transfer. Figure 8.18 shows the attitude of compromise in dealing with the Method Statement.

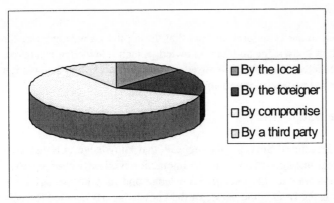

Figure 8.18 Compromise in dealing with the Method Statement

There is no doubt that knowledge transfer is a positive thing and is important because of the close relationship between knowledge transfer and economic development. An important majority of 71.65 percent of the responses in the study has confirmed the proposition. Figure 8.19 shows the result of knowledge transfer.

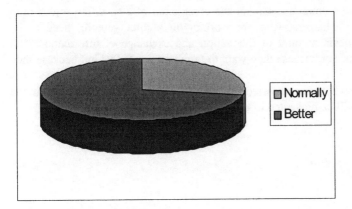

Figure 8.19 Consequence of knowledge transfer

Summary

This chapter has examined critical issues, certain elements and mechanisms of knowledge transfer in terms of:

What has been Transferred?

It has been confirmed in the Structured Survey that during the knowledge transfer process of both explicit knowledge and tacit knowledge, tacit knowledge is a major element that the transferees are most interested in along with explicit knowledge that has been transferred between foreign and local partners.

How was Knowledge Transferred?

The analysis of the Structured Survey data suggests that knowledge is transferred when foreign and local managers have intimate interaction while working together. However, different knowledge, i.e. explicit knowledge and tacit knowledge have different ways of transfer. In fact, the nature of the knowledge has decided the way of its transfer. Explicit knowledge is transferred in a formal or structured way while tacit knowledge is transferred in an informal manner, or a somewhat arbitrary manner.

Why was Knowledge Transferred?

It has been identified that motivation is an important issue in knowledge transfer. In order to achieve a common goal for the completion of a specific project, both foreign and local managers, who are working in a joint venture, need to be involved in significant amount of interaction and exchange of information, and knowledge transfer, not because they want to transfer knowledge, but because they have to.

The correlation between knowledge transfer and economic development in the three economies will be presented in Chapter 9.

Chapter 9

Correlation between Knowledge Transfer and Economic Development

Introduction

Following the presentation and interpretation of the data collected through the Structured Survey in Chapter 8, this Chapter will further explore the correlation between knowledge transfer and economic development. Firstly, this Chapter presents the correlation analysis between knowledge transfer and economic development by incorporating a Pearson Correlation analysis method. Secondly, the data collected from the survey, are discussed and analyzed by linking with the correlation presented previously. Thirdly, different implications in the three different economies are discussed by presenting bar charts of various answers to the research questions, which provide visual aids in understanding the relationships between knowledge transfer and economic development among the three regions in China. Finally the Chapter concludes with a summary.

Exploring the Correlation between Knowledge Transfer and Economic Development

In Chapter 7, the three geographical sources of data for the Structured Survey were described. These were the provinces of Jiangsu, Henan and the Xinjiang Autonomous Region. Furthermore, in the case of responses from Henan, a differentiation was made between those returned from the Xiaolangdi Project and "others". This was considered to be advisable, owing to the size and potential influence of the Xiaolangdi Project itself, and its potential for skewing the general response from Henan Province. It was considered to be potentially informative to explore the relationships between aspects of knowledge transfer and the level of economic development of each of the three geographical sources of data. To enable a more detailed analysis of the relationship between knowledge transfer and economic development, a correlation analysis was carried out with the economic indicators and the data derived from the three sample places, the measure of association adopted was Pearson's *r*. In order to do this, the first step was to construct a notional but valid scale of economic development. The basis of this scale was the economic data presented in Chapter 7, in particular the ten indicators of economic development obtained from the Construction Statistical Yearbook of China and presented in Table 7.2 of Chapter 7.

Creation of a Notional Scale of Economic Development

The ten indicators of economic development in construction in question are shown in Table 9.1.

1. Gross output value of construction (10000 yuan)
2. Number of projects (projects)
3. Construction quality projects (projects)
4. Statistics on machinery and equipment (pieces)
5. Value added of construction (10000 yuan)
6. Total floor space completed (10000 sqare metre)
7. Total capital and structure of total assets (10000 yuan)
8. Liabilities and creditors' equity (10000 yuan)
9. Total profit (10000 yuan)
10. Total number of construction enterprises (companies)

Table 9.1 Indicators of economic development

In each case, the results for Jiangsu, Henan and Xinjiang were computed as percentages of the national total figure. The resulting percentages were treated as relative development scores for each of the ten indicators, and on that basis were added to give an aggregate development score for each.

For simplicity in graphical scaling, the data were then simply transformed into a "normalised" index, with Jiangsu (raw score 1.0168) being treated as 100. This resulted in a "development index" for the three regions in question (Figure 9.3).

	Jiangsu	Henan	Xinjiang
1. Gross output value of construction	0.1174	0.0323	0.0125
2. Number of projects	0.0941	0.0438	0.0175
3. Construction quality projects	0.1110	0.0502	0.0129
4. Machinery and equipment	0.1001	0.0436	0.0115
5. Construction added value	0.1032	0.0313	0.0136
6. Floor space completed	0.1224	0.0387	0.0109
7. Total assets (10000 yuan)	0.0887	0.0261	0.0138
8. Investors' equity	0.1041	0.0241	0.0129
9. Total profit	0.1033	0.0237	-0.0040
10. Construction enterprises	0.0724	0.0448	0.0147
Aggregate score	**1.0168**	**0.3586**	**0.1163**

Table 9.2 Economic development scores for the three geographical data sources

Jiangsu	Henan	Xinjiang
100	35.27	11.44

Table 9.3 Notional development index for the three geographical data sources

Correlation of the Structured Survey Data with Notional Scores of Economic Development

Next, these newly created notional economic development indices for the geographical sources of data were tested for association with 19 of the 20[1] sets of responses from the survey. For the purpose, the CORREL function in Excel was used. This function (in common with most similar statistical routines) produces a value for Pearson's *product moment correlation coefficient*, *r*. This coefficient takes values from +1 to -1 and is given by

$$r = \frac{\sum (x_i - \bar{x})(y_i - \bar{y})}{(n-1)\, s_x\, s_y}$$

where $\sum x_i$ = sum of the variable x of all the n measurements, and
$\sum y_i$ = sum of the variable y of all the n measurements
s_x = standard deviation of x
s_y = standard deviation of y

---

[1] Question 1 of the inventory survey was an open question and no quantitative data resulted.

The sign (+ or -) indicates the *direction* of the relationship (positive or negative), and the number indicates the strength of the relationship. In the following analysis, values less than 0.3 have been described as "weak"; between 0.3 and 0.5 as "moderate"; 0.5 and 0.6 as "significant", and 0.7 and above as "strong". The results of the correlation are shown in Table 9.4.

Question	Answer	Jiangsu	Henan	Xinjiang	Pearson's *r*	Comment
How did you communicate Method Statement?	Formal document	65.64%	42.61%	41.58%	0.975	Strong +ve
	Sketch or note	19.63%	56.52%	32.67%	-0.578	Significant -ve
	Verbal	14.72%	0.87%	25.74%	-0.196	Weak -ve
Form of Method Statement	Handbook	22.44%	14.81%	9.00%	0.983	Strong +ve
	Previous MS	16.67%	16.10%	25.00%	-0.667	Significant -ve
	Contract document	55.77%	53.00%	45.00%	0.861	Strong +ve
	Handmade	5.13%	16.10%	21.00%	-0.999	Strong -ve
Main reason	Task Complex	18.52%	3.74%	4.00%	0.961	Strong +ve
	Resources	36.42%	33.64%	51.00%	-0.595	Significant-ve
	Work guidance	25.93%	11.21%	17.00%	0.788	Strong +ve
	Required by client	19.14%	51.40%	28.00%	-0.505	Significant -ve
Which party had the final say	Local	16.97%	4.58%	22.00%	-0.024	Weak -ve
	Foreign	24.85%	3.05%	30.00%	0.079	Weak +ve
	Together	58.18%	58.00%	48.00%	0.719	Strong +ve
Which party was mainly involved	Local	7.83%	30.75%	13.27%	-0.470	Moderate -ve
	Foreign	16.87%	12.25%	30.61%	-0.516	Significant -ve
	Together	75.30%	57.00%	56.12%	0.975	Strong +ve
Main needed knowledge	Cnstr. technology	16.56%	15.79%	30.69%	-0.675	Significant -ve
	Mgnt know-how	83.44%	84.21%	69.31%	0.675	Significant +ve
Main actual knowledge	Cnstr. technology	33.12%	33.70%	31.31%	0.524	Moderate +ve
	Mngt know-how	66.88%	66.30%	68.69%	-0.524	Moderate -ve
Main needed knowledge	Explicit	33.77%	68.22%	50.98%	-0.706	Strong -ve
	Tacit	66.23%	31.78%	49.02%	0.706	Strong +ve

Main actual knowledge	Explicit	48.08%	51.64%	46.32%	0.071	Weak +ve
	Tacit	51.92%	48.36%	53.68%	-0.070	Weak -ve
Main channel (explicit knowledge)	Conferences	29.80%	20.18%	30.61%	0.190	Weak +ve
	Meetings	30.46%	53.51%	13.27%	0.178	Weak +ve
	Seminars	27.81%	14.04%	50.00%	-0.387	Moderate -ve
	Training	11.92%	12.28%	6.12%	0.670	Significant +ve
Main channel (tacit knowledge)	Job training	17.86%	40.00%	12.12%	-0.064	Weak -ve
	Telephone	22.14%	19.23%	22.22%	0.235	Weak +ve
	Social	39.29%	20.51%	53.54%	-0.183	Weak -ve
	Chance meeting	20.71%	20.26%	12.12%	0.740	Strong +ve
Principal pattern of transfer	Foreign - local	28.66%	53.85%	28.28%	-0.245	Weak -ve
	Local - foreign	14.63%	7.69%	33.33%	-0.498	Moderate -ve
	2- way process	56.71%	38.46%	38.38%	0.967	Strong +ve
Main influencing factor	Culture	9.93%	13.33%	32.32%	-0.800	Strong -ve
	Language	30.46%	75.83%	25.25%	-0.166	Weak -ve
	Common objective	36.42%	5.00%	14.14%	0.853	Strong +ve
	Social values	23.18%	5.83%	28.28%	0.042	Weak +ve
Primary success factor	Mutual respect	18.13%	35.65%	35.42%	-0.962	Strong -ve
	Co-operation	60.63%	46.96%	48.96%	0.921	Strong +ve
	Co-ordination	21.25%	17.39%	15.63%	0.999	Strong +ve
Principal motivator	Mutual benefit	44.74%	24.37%	40.00%	0.466	Moderate +ve
	Collaboration	41.45%	24.37%	36.15%	0.538	Significant +ve
	Complete task	13.82%	51.26%	23.85%	-0.499	Moderate -ve
Principal issue resolved	Time	11.69%	2.88%	5.05%	0.877	Strong +ve
	Cost	22.08%	17.31%	23.23%	0.076	Weak +ve
	Safety	28.57%	36.54%	35.35%	-0.921	Strong -ve
	Quality	37.66%	43.27%	36.36%	-0.083	Weak -ve
Action with Method Statement after	Implemented	13.33%	17.05%	21.00%	-0.962	Strong -ve
	Revised	83.64%	61.24%	69.00%	0.819	Strong +ve
	Rejected	3.03%	21.71%	10.00%	-0.596	Significant-ve

If revised or	By the local	18.29%	10.75%	12.63%	0.875	Strong +ve
rejected how resolved	By foreigner	15.24%	14.55%	28.42%	-0.676	Significant -ve
	Compromise	61.59%	55.00%	48.42%	0.966	Strong +ve
	By third party	4.88%	19.70%	10.53%	-0.603	Significant -ve
Work carried out	Normally	29.88%	34.88%	29.00%	-0.122	Weak -ve
	Better	70.12%	65.12%	71.00%	0.122	Weak +ve

Table 9.4 The correlation between knowledge transfer and economic development in Jiangsu, Henan and Xinjiang, P.R.C.

There follows a step by step interpretation and analysis of the findings. Table 9.4 indicates a number of correlations between aspects of knowledge transfer and economic development in Jiangsu, Henan and Xinjiang. According to the correlation results shown in Table 9.4, which are self-explanatory, the relationship between certain aspects of knowledge transfer and economic development can be clearly predicated.

Examining the Relationships between Knowledge Transfer and Economic Development

In Chapter 7, based on the comprehensive analysis of the economic condition of Jiangsu Province, Henan Province and the Xinjiang Autonomous Region, it was concluded that Jiangsu Province is in the position of having a well developed economy, the Xinjiang Autonomous Region has a less developed economy, while Henan Province is in an intermediate position, with a newly developed economy. However, bearing in mind the correlation between knowledge transfer and economic development, the data allows us to make further comprehensive comparisons between the three economies in terms of perspectives, attitude, and philosophical concepts, towards the phenomenon and issues of knowledge transfer against the economic development levels.

In this section, it is intended to present and compare the different philosophy, attitude and perspective of people towards knowledge transfer issues in the different regions so as to identify various associations between knowledge transfer and economic development and the coherent relationship between explicit knowledge transfer and tacit knowledge transfer.

Reasons for Using a Method Statement

In the last section, the various reasons for using a Method Statement were explained in detail. Therefore, "reasons for using a Method Statement" will not be dwelt upon in order to avoid overlapping.

Form of the Method Statement

In Jiangsu and Henan, there is a clear tendency for construction people to prefer to communicate Method Statement through "formal document" rather than "sketch or note". People almost give up "verbal" mechanism to communicate the Method Statement. It should be pointed out that "verbal" communication of the Method Statement had been almost avoided in Henan. However, in the Xinjing Autonomous Region, "formal document", "sketch" or note" and "verbal" account for 41.58 percent, 32.67 percent and 25.74 percent respectively. Therefore, compared with Jiangsu and Henan, it seems that there is a lesser tendency for managers in Xinjiang to use "formal document" rather than "sketch or note" and "verbal". It is clear that the different attitude of using the Method Statement among the three regions implies that in a well developed economy people tend to communicate important issues in a structured way, while in a less developed economy people have not established the idea, namely that important issues should be dealt with appropriate mechanism. Figure 9.1 represents these different implications.

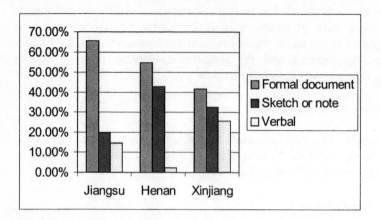

Figure 9.1 Comparison of form of the Method Statement

Foundation of the Method Statement

In terms of the foundation of Method Statements, a majority (53.37 percent) of responses indicated that the form of the Method Statement was mainly based upon "contract document", which confirms that the Method Statement is a part of the contract and a pre-requisite of doing a construction project. It should be noted that there is a high percentage of respondents in Xinjiang who indicate that the form of Method Statement is based on "handmade on spot". Henan is in the intermediate position, while Jiangsu does not favour having a Method Statement through "handmade on the spot". The different attitude towards this point suggests a strong correlation between knowledge transfer and economic development. Figure 9.2 represents the comparison of foundation of Method Statement.

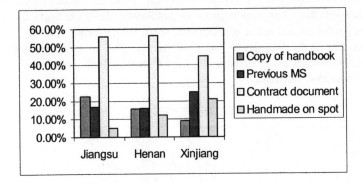

Figure 9.2 Comparison of foundation of the Method Statement

Further Reasons for Using a Method Statement

The respondents in the three regions held different views regarding the further reasons for using a Method Statement. Both Jiangsu and Xinjiang favoured "resource allocation" while Henan favoured "required by client". Figure 9.3 shows the different views about this issue.

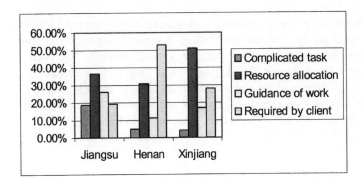

Figure 9.3 Comparison of further reasons for the Method Statement

Authority over a Method Statement

In terms of which party has the authority over the Method Statement, a general tendency confirmed by a dominant majority of 59.21 percent of the responses is that the foreign and local partners should work together closely and make decisions together, while in the study 18.34 percent of the responses favour the local party and 22.34 percent of the responses still favour the foreign partner. However, Henan province prevails over the other two regions in supporting the view that "the foreign and local parties should work together and solve the problems together". This data implies that in the less developed economy, people are still confused about the mechanism of knowledge transfer. Figure 9.4 shows which party has the authority over the Method Statement.

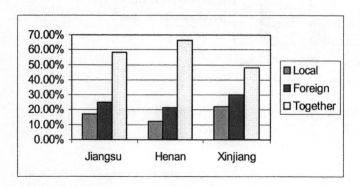

Figure 9.4 Comparison of authority over the Method Statement

Parties Involved with the Method Statement

A dominated majority (67.61 percent) of the responses confirmed the need for both the foreign and local partners to discuss Method Statements together and solve problems together. It should be noted that the attitude towards this issue is positively related with economic development. The "together" columns have formed a ladder with Jiangsu at the top, Henan in the middle and Xinjiang at the bottom. This data suggest that knowledge transfer and economic development has a strong relationship and is positively effected (please refer to Figure 9.5).

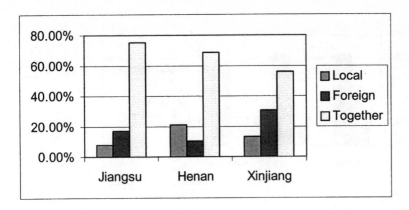

Figure 9.5 Parties mainly involved

What is Being Transferred?

Based upon the study, it is reasonable to assume that knowledge transfer occurs during the implementation of contracts of international joint - venture projects. However, the data analysis of the present research suggests that the transfer of management know-how overwhelmingly dominates the process of knowledge transfer. It should be noted that there is high demand for construction technology in Xinjiang while there is a high demand for management know-how both in Jiangsu and in Henan. This data suggest that there is more demand for tacit knowledge in a well developed economy while there is more demand of explicit knowledge in a less developed economy. Figure 9.6 represents what is needed to be transferred whereas Figure 9.7 represents what actually did transfer in practice.

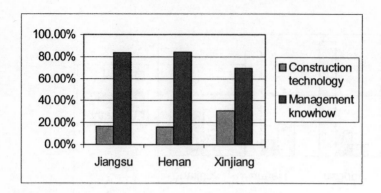

Figure 9.6 Comparison of what needed to transfer

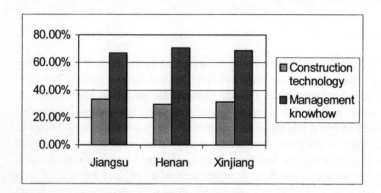

Figure 9.7 Comparison of what did actually transfer

Explicit Knowledge or Tacit Knowledge?

The comparison of the data suggests that the transfer of tacit knowledge dominates the process of knowledge transfer. However, there is a hesitation among people to express their views towards explicit and tacit knowledge transfer. In particular, this is the case in Xinjiang, where people are not clear about the concept of explicit and tacit knowledge. However, there is a clear tendency in Jiangsu that people have a significant demand for the transfer of tacit knowledge while Henan still remains in the intermediate position. Figure 9.8 shows what is needed to be transferred while

Figure 9.9 shows what did actually transfer in practice in terms of explicit and tacit knowledge.

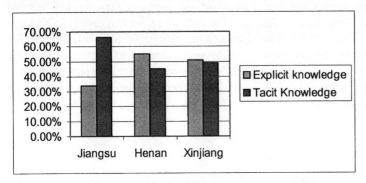

Figure 9.8 Comparison of what needed to be transferred

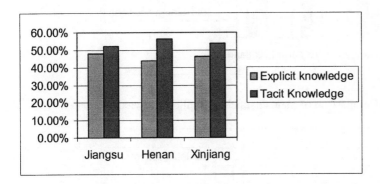

Figure 9.9 Comparison of what did actually transfer

How was Knowledge Transferred?

It has been identified that both explicit knowledge and tacit knowledge have special ways of transfer. There is no agreement regarding the main channel of transfer among the regions. However, the data show that construction people in Henan believe "meeting" is the main channel of explicit knowledge transfer while in Xinjiang believe "seminar" is the main channel of explicit knowledge transfer. In Henan it is believed that "job training" is the main channel of tacit knowledge transfer while Jiangsu and Xinjiang believe "social occasion" is the main channel of tacit knowledge transfer.

The analysis suggests that knowledge transfer is a "two-way process". However, construction managers in Henan strongly believe that knowledge transfer take place "from foreign partners to local partners" while in Xinjiang they feel that there is transfer from "local to foreign". These data suggest that people in Xinjiang are still unclear about the basic elements and the definitions of knowledge transfer. Figure 9.10 shows the comparison of the main channel of explicit knowledge transfer, Figure 9.11 shows the comparison of the main channel of tacit knowledge transfer, while Figure 9.12 shows the comparison of the principal pattern of knowledge transfer.

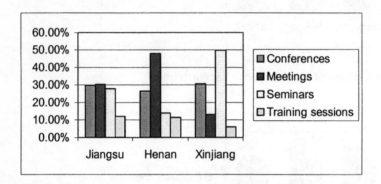

Figure 9.10 Comparison of main channels of explicit knowledge transfer

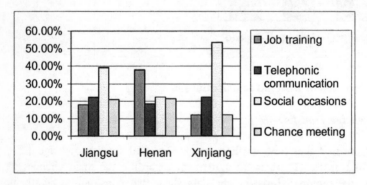

Figure 9.11 Comparison of main channels of tacit knowledge transfer

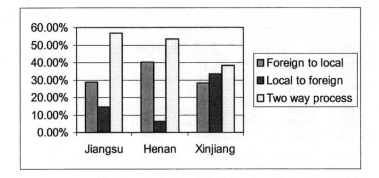

Figure 9.12 Comparison of the principal patterns of knowledge transfer

Success of Knowledge Transfer

In terms of which factor is the main influencing factor in knowledge transfer, it should be pointed out that a clear majority (75.83 percent) of responses in Henan believe that "language" is the main influencing factor and 36.42 percent of responses in Jiangsu believed that "common objective" is the main influencing factor, whereas 32.32 percent of the responses in Xinjing believed that "culture" is the main influencing factor. In terms of a principal factor in achieving a successful knowledge transfer, however, there is an agreement that "close co-operation" is the primary factor in achieving successful knowledge transfer. In terms of a principal motivator in achieving successful knowledge transfer, it is notable that in Jiangsu 44.74 percent of the respondents favours "mutual benefit", while in Henan 51.26 percent of the respondents favours "completion task", and in Xinjiang 40.00 percent of the respondents favours "mutual benefit". Figure 9.13 shows the argument over the issue among the three regions. Figure 9.14 shows the comparison over the primary factor in achieving a successful knowledge transfer while Figure 9.15 shows the argument over the principal motivator in achieving successful knowledge transfer.

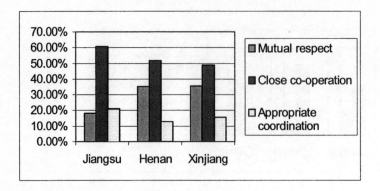

Figure 9.13 Comparison of main influencing factors

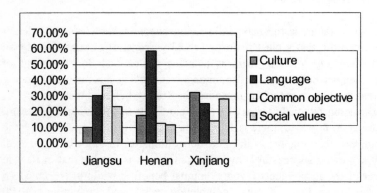

Figure 9.14 Comparison of principal factor in achieving successful knowledge transfer

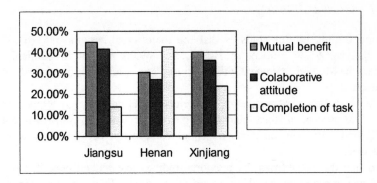

Figure 9.15 Comparison of principal motivator in achieving successful knowledge transfer

Key and Critical Issues

It seems that there is agreement that the construction mangers in Xinjiang, Henan and Jiangsu pay attention to quality, safety, cost and time. However the degree of attention to the above four issues decreases gradually from "quality" to "time". Figure 9.16 shows the comparison of these particular issues.

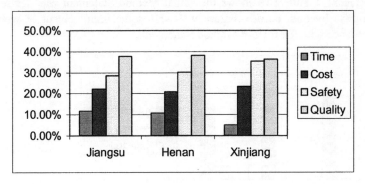

Figure 9.16 Comparison of the key and critical issues

Aftermath of Knowledge Transfer

An interesting finding of this study is that the majority of respondents, (83.64 percent in Jiangsu, 61.24 percent in Henan, and 69.00 percent in Xinjiang), confirmed that the Method Statement will be revised as a result of discussion of the Method Statement.

If this Method Statement was revised or rejected, the majority (61.59 percent in Jiangsu, 55.00 percent in Henan and 48.42 percent in Xinjiang) confirmed that the actual Method Statement was devised through compromise between the foreign and local partners.

It seems that this reconfirms the previous findings that mutual benefit, close co-operation and appropriate coordination are the important factors in achieving a successful knowledge transfer.

No doubt knowledge transfer is a positive thing and bears significant consequences because of the close relationship between technology transfer and economic growth. The majority (70.12 percent in Jiangsu, 75.12 percent in Henan and 71.00 percent in Xinjiang) has confirmed the proposition. Figure 9.17 shows the result of discussing the Method Statement leads to the revision of the Method Statement. However, this issue is also positively related with economic development, as the "revised" columns have formed a ladder with Jiangsu at the top, Henan at the middle and Xinjiang at the bottom. If the Method Statement was revised or rejected, Figure 9.18 shows the actual Method Statement was devised through comprise by both parties. Figure 9.19 shows the improvement of work done in accordance with the revised Method Statement.

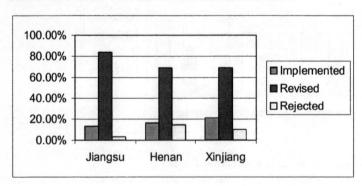

Figure 9.17 Result of discussing the Method Statement leads to revision of it

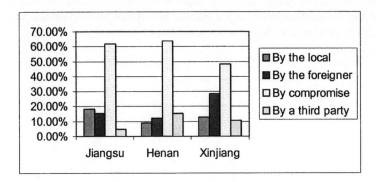

Figure 9.18 The actual Method Statement was devised through comprise

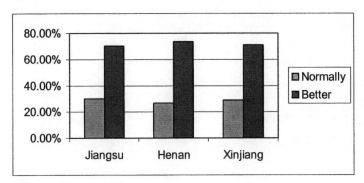

Figure 9.19 Improvement of work done in accordance with the revised Method Statement

It should be pointed out that all the figures and the bar charts mentioned above have formed interesting patterns, associations and correlation, which will be presented in Chapter 10.

Summary

It has been identified from the correlation analysis of the three regions, in terms of knowledge transfer and economic development, that there is strong association between economic development and a number of aspects of knowledge transfer, such as, people's attitudes, perspectives and philosophical concepts towards the phenomenon and issues of knowledge transfer. Furthermore, the comprehensive comparison and analysis of the data collected from the three regions presented the figures indicate a similar consequence.

However, the relationship between knowledge transfer and economic development and the relationship between transfer of explicit knowledge and tacit knowledge will be presented in detail in the next Chapter.

Chapter 10

Conclusion

Introduction

Firstly, this chapter re-examines the aims and objectives of the current study. Following that, the chapter discusses the implications of a relationship between knowledge transfer and economic development and a relationship between explicit knowledge transfer and tacit knowledge transfer in the context of a systematic approach to tacit knowledge transfer. The effect of the the Xiaolangdi project itself on responses from Henan will be explored. The chapter then discusses the implications of policy and practice. Finally the chapter presents an assessment of the contribution to knowledge of the study and suggestions for further research.

Aims and Objectives are Examined

The aim of the study (re-stated from Chapter 1) was to investigate the current mechanisms of technology transfer and the aspects of technology transfer between foreign and local managers within international joint-ventures in China. The aim has therefore been achieved step by step based on: 1. The establishment of a theoretical framework for analysing the technology transfer process of the construction industry between developed and developing countries; 2. A Case Study that was undertaken on the Sino-foreign joint-venture demonstration project at Xiaolangdi; 3. A Structured Survey that was carried out in Xinjiang, Henan and Jiangsu, People's Republic of China.

The objectives of the study are therefore re-stated here for convenience of discussion in this chapter. They were:

- From the literature, to establish a theoretical framework for the tracking of the technology transfer process.
- To discern the basic patterns of knowledge transfer through a Case Study.
- To evaluate the appropriateness and effectiveness of the study by using a Structured Survey.
- To identify the implications of the relationship between technology transfer and economic development levels.

The extent to which these objectives have been achieved will now be examined, taking the objectives one at a time.

Objective 1

A theoretic framework for tracking of the technology transfer process has been established in the study through an extensive review of the literature and the current state of knowledge of technology transfer. What has become apparent is that knowledge transfer is crucial during the process of technology transfer *as knowledge is the key to control over technology as a whole.*

Objective 2

The basic patterns of knowledge transfer have been discerned through the semi-structured interviews of foreign and local managers at Xiaolangdi during the Case Study. Furthermore, a typical management structure of Sino-foreign joint venture in Xiaolangdi was developed, which has provided a platform for the identification of the physical structure of the dyadic interaction.

Objective 3

Following the study of economic indicators of construction industry in Xinjiang, Henan and Jiangsu and based on a Structured Survey in these three regions, the appropriateness and effectiveness of the study was evaluated by examining the process of dealing with the construction Method Statement. The result of the study among the three regions has indicated a strong correlation between knowledge transfer and economic development, which will be discussed in the Section of Research Findings of this Chapter. Furthermore, the process of knowledge transfer was further defined with the establishment of the concept and significance of tacit knowledge transfer.

Objective 4

The relationship between technology transfer and economic development was explored through the analyses of the data collected in the Structured Survey by using the correlation technique of Pearson's Product-Moment Correlation Coefficient. Moreover, implications of relationship between transfer of explicit and tacit knowledge have been identified. However, the following text will further explain the issues of aims and objectives of the current study and the research findings.

Research Findings

What is the relationship between knowledge transfer and economic development? Are they positively or negatively related, or is the relationship more complicated? Based on the data obtained from both the Case Study and the Structured Survey, this section will answer these questions.

The Relationship between Knowledge Transfer and Economic Development is Defined

The study of construction activities with a comparison of the economic indicators among Jiangsu Province, Henan Province and the Xinjiang Autonomous Region suggests a notional hierarchy of economic development. Jiangsu is at the higher level with Xinjiang at the lower level, and Henan is in the middle position. Analysis and comparison of the data collected from the three regions suggests that certain aspects of knowledge transfer are paralleled by the notional progression of economic development. In other words, there are features of knowledge transfer that appear to be associated with levels of economic development. To put it differently, this relationship between knowledge transfer and economic development is positively effected. Figure 10.1 represents a simplified view of the relationship between knowledge transfer and economic growth. The arrow in the figure indicates that the demand for knowledge transfer grows as the economy increases.

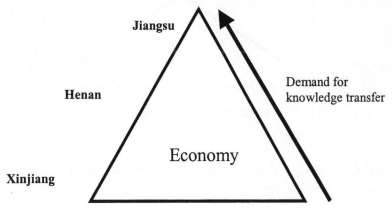

Figure 10.1. Relationship (notional hypotheses) between knowledge transfer and economic development

In Chapter 9 (Table 9.4; Figure 9.1; Figure 9.2; Figure 9.4, Figure 9.5; Figure 9.12; Figure 9.17) the results showed clear relationships as presented in Figure 10.1. between aspects of knowledge transfer and the different levels of economic development as exemplified by the three regions under examination. These aspects are now connected in more details.

The Relationship between Transfer of Explicit Knowledge and Tacit Knowledge is Examined

A comparison based on economic indicators of the three regions suggests that in a well-developed region there is more demand for tacit knowledge transfer, while there is more demand for explicit knowledge transfer in the less developed region. In other words, people in the most developed economies are keen to obtain tacit knowledge (soft knowledge), such as management know-how, while people in the least developed economies are keen to obtain explicit knowledge (hard technology), such as a specific technology to manufacture a product. Thus, the relationship between the need for tacit knowledge transfer and explicit knowledge transfer is X-Shaped. This is shown diagrammatically in Figure 10.2.

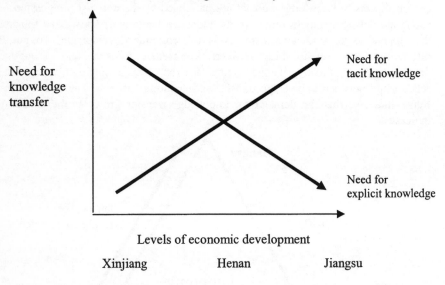

Figure 10.2 Relationship (notional hypotheses) between tacit knowledge transfer and explicit knowledge transfer

In Chapter 9 (Figure 9.6 and Figure 9.8) the results showed a clear relationship as presented in Figure 10.2 between tacit knowledge transfer and explicit knowledge transfer as exemplified by the three regions under examination.

Based on the above, it is suggested that the desire to obtain more tacit knowledge increases and the desire to obtain more explicit knowledge decreases with the levels of economic development. In other words, in a developing economy, people are more thirsty for explicit or hard knowledge, such as a specific technology to manufacture a product that enables people to survive rather than for tacit or soft knowledge, such as management know-how that enables an economy to have sustainable growth.

Systematic Approach to Tacit Knowledge Transfer

It has been recognised from the Case Study and the Structured Survey of the research project that tacit knowledge transfer is often blocked due to the very nature of that form of knowledge. However, as identified in the studies, there are certain channels of tacit knowledge transfer, such as, "telephonic communication", "social occasions", and "chance meeting at work" (refer to Figure 6.4). This suggests that the channels of tacit knowledge transfer appear to work currently in a somewhat arbitrary manner. It is reasonable to suggest that the transfer of tacit knowledge can be more systematised. Figure 10.3 represents a systematic model of tacit knowledge transfer, where certain influencing factors, motivation and congruence of knowledge transfer have been highlighted.

For those wishing to encourage the transfer of knowledge, it would be helpful to adopt a more systematic approach that deals with the multi-faceted aspects of knowledge transfer. Such a systematic approach would consider all available resources, constraints, relationships, motivators, influencing factors, channels and foreseeable contingencies as a part of a dynamic whole in order to arrive at the most effective and efficient means of meeting the knowledge transfer objectives. The successful implementation of knowledge transfer on a joint - venture project requires an understanding of the objectives and the challenges facing the project's working environment, and requires the application of conceptual skills, relevant and adequate systems, and information technology tools and concepts.

Effect of the Xiaolangdi Project on Responses from Henan

As previously established, the Xiaolangdi project was considered by the Chinese Government as an excellent example of the practice of international project management. During the implementation of the project, thousands of young engineers have been trained and have acquired both professional knowledge and management expertise. As Zhang (1997) points out, "it will be a great and an arduous task to assess the social and economic result of knowledge transfer in the Xiaolangdi project. It is necessary to establish a research institute, which will promote international project management research and summarises the international project management experience of the Xiaolangdi project in a systematic way and provide guidance in theory and practice in the future".

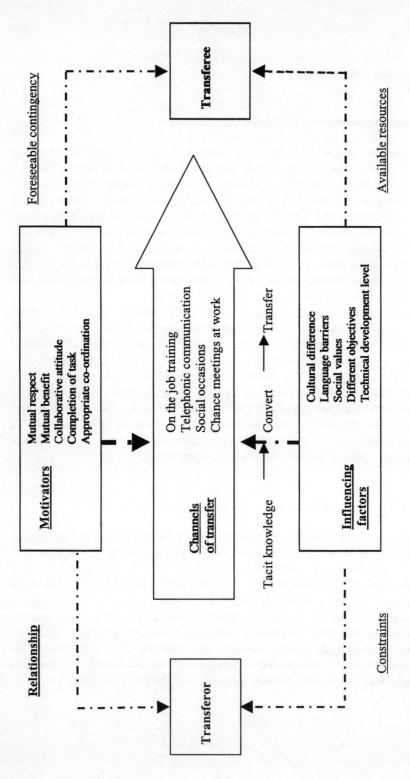

Figure 10.3 A model of tacit knowledge transfer

Experts with the consultancy group of the World Bank confirmed after a recent examination that construction on the Xiaolangdi Water Control Project, a key project to harness the sand silting of the Yellow River's bed, has brought no damage to the surrounding environment since it started six years ago. Harvey F. Ludwig, chief expert of the group, indicated that tests by the experts of the World Bank show that all the indexes of the project have reached the world standard in terms of environmental protection. It is clear that the authority's the measures to protect the environment have been well carried out during the construction work. Ludwig at Harvard University and a famous specialist, confirmed that the work on environmental protection at Xiaolangdi is most likely to become a model for other project constructions in China. Appraisal of the teamwork of the Xiaolangdi Project by the current Deputy President of the World Bank has suggested the successful transfer of management know-how between the local and foreign partners. The collaborative attitudes of both foreign and local partners has been highly valued and appreciated. The Xiaolangdi project was completed quickly and effectively. The Xiaolangdi project was let under international competition. As far as the project is concerned, what the World Bank has brought in is not only the funding for the construction of the project itself, but also access to advanced technology and management expertise, which has created a platform for domestic and international contractors to have technical co-operation, technology and knowledge transfer, and competition. Among all the projects founded by the World Bank, the Xiaolangdi project has been a particular success in terms of time, cost and quality. The great achievement of which has not only set up a good example in the hydro-power construction in China, but also has significance in the world (Gouna, 2000).

The analysis of the data, as it stands, from the beginning to the end of the Structured Survey shows that Henan Province is in a superior position in terms of various issues, such as attitude, interest, perspective and motivation towards knowledge transfer though economic development level is in the intermediate position. Why is Henan Province always in a predominant position? (Refer to Figure 8.2, Figure 8.4, Figure 8.6, Figure 8.8, Figure 8.18 and Figure 8.19 in Chapter 8). The most obvious interpretation is that the Xiaolangdi project itself has made a significant impact on the Province. The Xiaolangdi project, located in Henan Province, involved thousands of people (technical and administrative) from the Province during the implementation of the project. The fact is that local people and foreigners worked together for the common goal to achieve a successful project. When people were exposed to a certain culture or environment, the philosophy, perspective and way of thinking would be affected in a certain way. This again proves that knowledge transfer did occur during the implementation of the project and the positive effect of knowledge transfer as well.

Implication for Policy and Practice

Knowledge transfer has been shown to be positively effected by the levels of economic development of the recipients. As discussed in the last chapter, in terms of the communication of the Method Statement, there exists a large gap between Jiangsu, Henan and Xinjiang. In Jiangsu, construction people rarely use "verbal" mechanisms to communicate the Method Statement; in Henan, construction people avoid "verbal". However, there is a strong tendency in Xinjiang for using the "verbal" mechanism rather than a "formal document" (refer to Figure 8.1). Knowledge transfer is a two-way process. However, it appears that construction people in Xinjiang feel that there is "knowledge transfer from local to foreign" while construction people in Henan strongly believe that there is "knowledge transfer from foreign to local". Construction people in Jiangsu support the idea that knowledge transfer takes place from foreign to local.

    Given the situation that a joint-venture is a preferred vehicle for technology transfer to China, it is reasonable to suggest that it would be wise and practical to promote the establishment of joint ventures between Xinjiang and Jiangsu, or between Xinjiang and Henan rather than to promote setting up joint ventures between, for example, Xinjiang and western countries. Figure 10.4 suggests effective models of setting-up international joint ventures and domestic joint ventures. It has been recognised that knowledge transfer is not obtainable if the gap is too big in terms of economic development between transferor and transferee, despite the governments and funding agencies that promote technology transfer. It appears that there are 20,500 Sino-foreign joint-ventures in Jiangsu and 2000 Sino-foreign joint ventures in Henan, which are operating effectively and efficiently, while statistics show that there were no Sino-foreign joint-ventures existing in Xinjiang till 1998 (refer to Chapter 7). Of course it has been recognised in the study that the joint ventures between Jiangsu, Henan and the West are an effective approach for transferring technology and developing the economy.

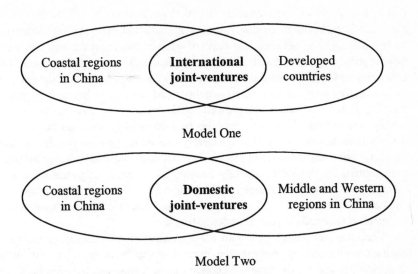

Figure 10.4 Effective models of joint-ventures

Contribution to the Understanding of How Knowledge is Transferred

Because of the inability to meet the demands of economic growth from current indigenous resources, the Chinese construction industry relies on foreign investment in its various forms. This is a short-term measure, but in the long-term China seeks the additional benefit of sustainable technology transfer. There are various modes of international activity that could have an effect. Of these, international joint ventures appear to be the preferred vehicle for both the recipients in question - China - and of its major external funding agency of construction activity - the World Bank.

This potential is recognised by the World Bank. In 1993 the Bank adopted an explicit policy of requiring a commitment to technology transfer from its contractors to the construction industries of the host country. According to Abbott (1985), an essential condition for effecting such technology transfer is the clear specification of the requirement in a contract. The World Bank's policy in principle was that organisations should not be awarded contracts without forming meaningful partnerships with local companies. Despite the existence of the policy there appears to be few, if any mechanisms for ensuring that technology transfer has actually taken place or to measure its appropriateness and effectiveness. The World Bank has itself already recognised the difficulties in monitoring such a policy. Yet this deficiency results from the belief that there is something inherent in the technology that determines the effectiveness of transfer. This research supports the view that the nature of the technology is not a major factor. In fact, the field-work undertaken in China as part of this research, gives a clear indication that it is quantity of knowledge transfer that predominantly affects the success of the technology transfer. In fact, it further appears that there is a pronounced effect in the relationship between the type of knowledge required and the technical development of the recipients. An important contribution of this research to the efficiency of the Chinese construction industry has been to analyse the components of knowledge transfer and determine how and why it is being inhibited. The tracking of *Method Statements* showed that in general, explicit knowledge is being readily transferred. However, it is the tacit knowledge that has been neglected. Results from the fieldwork showed clearly that there were no systematic channels for tacit knowledge transfer in place. This fact could have an adverse influence on the potential for inward technology transfer. Tacit knowledge has not even been recognised as an important factor and its transfer has been merely reliant on chance encounters. To improve its delivery, this study points out that a more systematic approach is required for tacit knowledge transfer.

Therefore, in association with the specification of technology transfer in a contract addressed by Abbott, the current research project has established a framework to specify the terms and conditions of technology transfer. Furthermore, the study has clearly pointed out that knowledge transfer is crucial during the process of technology transfer during the implementation of joint-venture projects. Without knowledge transfer, technology transfer will not work.

Theoretical Contribution

This study has provided an original contribution towards an understanding of the process of technology transfer. In addition, this study has made a further investigation into the mechanisms of the tacit knowledge transfer between international joint-venture partners. The Case Study, the Structured Survey and the evaluation of the research model for the present research, which were designed to take place within the context of three different economies in China, are coherently related, and therefore the aims and objectives of the research project have been achieved. It is believed that this cross-culture research with the application of a psychological methodology proves successful. From an academic point of view, the study has produced insights into the transfer of tacit knowledge that had not existed hitherto in an area that has attracted little previous research. The present research focuses on the way that technology transfer has developed into knowledge transfer, in particular, tacit knowledge transfer, which is at the forefront of research in this area.

Furthermore, the relationship between knowledge transfer and economic growth and the relationship between explicit knowledge and tacit knowledge has provided further insights and grounding for the theorists and economists to address economic issues both at macro-economic and micro-economic levels.

Practical Contribution

It should be noted that this study has provided a useful contribution to tracking the process of technology transfer in practice. The distinctiveness of the research programme lies in that the understanding of tacit knowledge transfer, which has been developed and evaluated within the three different economies, will enable the recipients and donor organisations as well as international funding agencies to identify the essential ingredients of a particular aspect of technology transfer, namely the transfer of tacit knowledge. It is believed that the theoretical framework of the research may provide guidance and enable policy-makers within the governments, sponsors of projects and the executives of the companies involved to address the existing deficiencies in the process of technology transfer, and assist in development of more appropriate arrangement for the transfer of management knowledge.

Recommendations for Further Research

The boundary of the current research has been set within the context of construction industry in the People's Republic of China. However, the qualitative data has been collected and followed by a comprehensive quantitative analysis and comparison. It is hoped that based on the advances made in the study, the practical assessment of management know-how and the further tracking of the process of tacit knowledge can be approached in future research. Ideally, the sampling places for undertaking major studies would be three different economies in different countries, possibly representing advanced industrialised countries (AICs), newly developed countries (NDCs) and less developed countries (LDCs), rather than three regions in China.

Bibliography

Books

Agmon, T. and Von Glinow (1991) *Technology Transfer in International Business.* London: Oxford University Press.

Athey, T. (1974) *Systematic Systems Approach.* Englewood Cliffs, NJ: Prentice-Hall.

Austen, A.D., and Neale, R.H. (1995) *Managing Construction Projects – A Guide to Processes and Procedures,* International Labour Office Geneva.

Barrett, P. (1993) *Profitable Practice Management For the Construction Professional.* London: E & FN Spon.

Bennet, J. (1991) *International Construction Project Management General Theory and Practice.* London: Butterworth-Heinemann Ltd.

Bradbury, F.R. (1978) *Technology Transfer Practice of International Firms.* Netherlands: Sijthoff & Noordhoff International Publishers BV.

Cater, D.C. (1997) *Doing Quantitative Psychological Research: From Design to Report,* East Sussex: Psychology Press Publishers.

Cohen, R. J., Swerdlik, M. E., and Phillips, S.M. (1996) *Psychological Testing and Assessment – An Introduction to Tests and Measurement.* Mayfield Publishing Company.

Coombs, R., Richard, A., Saviotti, P.P., and Walsh, V. (1996) *Technological Collaboration: The Dynamics of Co-operation in Industrial Innovation.* London: Edward Elgar Publishing Limited.

Coskun, S.A. (1985) *Technology Transfer Geographic, Economic, Cultural, and Technical Dimensions.* London: Greenwood Press.

Davenport, T.H. and Prusak, L. (1998) *Working Knowledge, How Organisation Manage What they Know.* Harvard Business School Press, Boston.

Dodgson, M., and Rothwell, R. (1993) *Innovation in the Construction Sector.* The Handbook of Industrial Innovation. London: Edward Elgar Publishing Limited.

Dougherty, V. (1999) *Industrial and Commercial Training.* Volume 31. Number 7. 1999, pp. 262-266. MCB University Press.

Downs, C. W., Wine, S., and Greenbaum, H. H. (1994) *Communication Research Measures - A Sourcebook.* The Guilford Press.

Drewer, S. (1982) *The Transfer of Construction Techniques to Developing Countries - The Role of Expatriate Architects, Consultants and Contractors.* London: Lund Humphries.

Flanagan, R., and Li, S.R. (1997) *International Construction: A Perspective of China.* Ascot: The Chartered Institute of Building.

Gao, J. (1997) *The Analyses of Technology Innovation of Chinese Enterprises.* Beijing: Tsinghua University Press.

Gatchel, R.J., and Mears, F.G. (1982) *Personality - Theory, Assessment, and Research*. St. Martin's Press: New York.

Goodwin, R. (1996) *A Brief Guide to Cross-cultural Psychological Research. Psychological Research-Innovative Methods and Strategies*. Routledge: London.

Gray, J., and White, G. (1982) *China's New Development Strategy*. London: Academic Press.

Gudykunst, W.B. (1998) *Bridging Differences – Effective Inter-group Communication*. London: SAGE Publications Thousand Oaks.

Hargie, O., Saunders, C., and Dickson, D. (1994) *Social Skills in Interpersonal Communication*. London and New York: Routledge.

Harvey R. C., and Ashworth, A. (1993) *The Construction Industry of Great Britain*. London: Butterworth-Heinemann Ltd.

Hillebrandt P. M., and Cannon, J. (1990) *The Modern Construction Firm*. London: The Macmillan Press Ltd.

Hofstede, G. (1980) *Culture's Consequences: International Differences in Work-related Values*. Beverly Hills, CA: Sage.

Holt, G.D. (1997) *A Guide to Successful Dissertation Study for Students of the Built Environment*. University of Wolverhampton, UK.

International Labour Organisation (1983) *Management Training for the Construction industry in Developing Countries*. Geneva: International Labour Organisation.

Langford, D.A., and Rowland, V.A. (1995) *Managing Overseas Construction Contracting*. London: Thomas Telford.

Lee, J.C., (1990) *Essentials of Psychological Testing*. Harper & Row: New York.

Leonard-Barton, D. (1995) *Wellsprings of Knowledge: Building and Sustaining the Resources of Innovation*. Harvard University Press.

Li, H. (1997) *Management for International Project-Contracting*. Beijing: China Building Industry Press.

Li, H. (1989) *Practical Psychology in Construction Management*. Beijing: China Building Industry Press.

Liu, M.S. (1997) *Strategy and Management of Multi-national Enterprises*. Shanghai: Lixin Accounting Press.

Ma, H. (1997) *Economic Situation and Prospect of China*. Beijing: China Development Press.

Maitland, A. (1999) *Management of Knowledge Management: Lessons can be Learned & Failed Attempts to Capture and Use Employees' Knowledge*. Management and Technology, *The Financial Times*.

Melvin, T. (1979) *Practical Psychology in Construction Management*. New York: Van Nostrand Reinhold Company.

Miles, D. (1995) *Constructive Change: Managing International Technology Transfer*, International Labour Office Geneva.

Miles, D., and Neale, R. (1991) *Building for Tomorrow: International Experience in Construction Industry Development*. Geneva: International Labour Office.

Mnaas, C. (1990) *Technology Transfer in the Developing Countries.* London: The Macmillan Press Ltd.

Parr, R.L., and Sullivan, P.H. (1996) *Technology Licensing Corporate Strategies for Maximizing Value.* London: John Wiley & Sons.

Polanyi, M. (1967) *The Tacit Dimension.* Routledge & Kegan Paul Ltd, London.

Rosenberg, N., and Frischtak, C. (1985) *International Technology Transfer Concept, Measures and Comparisons.* New York: Praeger Publishers.

Razvigorova, E., and Wolf-Laudon, G. (1991) *East-West Joint Ventures. The Business Environment.* International Institute for Applied Systems Analysis Basil Blackwell, Inc. Cambridge, Mass: Blackwells.

Reddy, A.C., 1996, *A Macro Prospective on Technology Transfer.* Quorum: Westport, CT.

Robertshaw, J., Mecca, S., and Rerick, M. (1978) *Problem-solving: A System Approach.* New York: Petroocelli.

Samli, A. (1985) *Technology Transfer: Geographic, Economic, Cultural and Technical Dimensions.* Greenwood Press, USA.

Schleifer, T.G. (1990) *Contractors' Survival Guide: Manage with Confidence.* London: John Wiley & Sons.

Sharif, N. (1983) *Management of Technology Transfer and Development.* ESCAP Regional Centre for Technology Transfer, Bangalore.

Singer, H.W. (1991) *Joint Ventures and Collaborations.* New Delhi: Indus Publishing Company.

Steward, T.A. (1998) Intellectual Capital: *The New Wealth of Organisation,* Nicholas Brearley, London.

Suchman, L. (1987) *Plans and Situated Actions.* New York: Cambridge University Press.

Tashakkori, A. and Teddle, C. (1998) *Mixed Methodology – Combining Qualitative and quantitative approaches.* SAGE Publication, Inc. London.

Tseng,W., Khor, H.E., Kochhar, K., Mihailek, D., and Burton, D. (1994) *Economic Reform in China: A New Phase.* International Monetary Fund. Washington DC.

Van Gundy, A.B. (1988) *Techniques of Structured Problem Solving.* New York: Van Nostrand Reinhold.

Vaus, D.A. (2001) *Research Design in Social Research.* SAGE Publications London, Thousand Oaks, New Delhi.

Woodwind, J.F. (1997) *Construction Project Management: Getting it Right First Time.* London: Thomas Telford.

Warren, R.H. (1989) *Motivation and Productivity in the Construction Industry.* New York: Van Nostrand Reinhold.

Whyte, W.F. (1997) *Creative Problem Solving in the Field – Reflections on a Career.* SAGE Publication, Inc., London.

Yin, R.K. (1994) *Case Study Research-design and Methods.* SAGE Publication, Thousand Oaks, London New Delhi.

Yu, X.Y. (1990) *International Economic Law.* Nanjing University Press.

Zhang, M.Q. (1987) *International Technology Trade.* Beijing: Foreign Trade and Education Press.

Journals

Antikainen, J. (1993) 'Technology Transfer to Developing Countries'. *Energy World* 213 pp.6-9.

Arditi, D., and Mochtar, K. (1996) 'Productivity Improvement in the Indonesian Construction Industry', *Construction Management and Economics*.

Badaracco, J.L., Jr. (1991) 'The Knowledge Link: How Firms Compete through Strategic Alliances'. Boston: *Harvard Business Press*.

Bakuli, D.L. (1994) 'Pitfalls in Technology Transfer: Kenya's Construction Industry'. *World Development*, 22, 10, pp.1609-1612.

Baldassini, N. (1995) 'Interaction Technology/Technology Interaction'. *Techniques and Architecture*, No.422, pp.68-75.

Berger, M. (1998) 'Going Global: Implications for Communication and Leadership'. *Training, Industrial and Commercial Training*.

Bon, R. (1997) 'The Future of International Construction'. *Building Research and Information*, p.139.

Bon, R. (1996) 'Whither Global Construction? Some Results of the ECERU opinion survey 1993-1995'. *Building Research and Information*. Volume (24). No.2 p.6.

Carillo, P. (1996) 'Technology Transfer on Joint-venture Projects in Developing Countries'. *Construction Management and Economics,* 14(1) January pp.45-54.

Carrillo, P. (1994) 'Technology Transfer: A Survey of International Construction Companies'. *Construction Management and Economics*, 12, pp.45-51.

Carrillo, P. (1993) 'Technology Transfer Mechanisms for Construction Industry in Developing Countries'. *Science, Technology & Development*, Vol.11, No.1, pp.1-14. London: Frank Cass.

Chen, J.J. (1997) 'The Impact of Chinese Economic Reform upon the Construction Industry. Building Research and Information'. *The International Journal of Research Development and Demonstration*, Volume 25, No.4.

Chen, J.J. (1996) 'The Impact of Public Construction Investment upon Special Economic Zones-The Chinese Experience'. *Construction Management and Economics*, 14. pp.175-182.

Chen, J.J. (1997) 'China's Construction Industry and Foreign Investment' Building Research and Information'. *The International Journal of Research Development and Development and Demonstration*, Volume 25, No.1.

Cushman, N., Nam, C., and Tatum, C. (1992) 'Technology Transfer in Building Control: A Case of Seismic Design'. *Journal of Construction, Engineering and Management*, 118-1, pp.129-141.

Darrah, C.N. (1995) 'Workplace Training, Workplace Learning: A Case Study', *Human Organisation*, Vol.54, No. 11995.

Davidson, W.H., and McFetridge, D. G. (1985) 'Key Characteristics in the Choice of International Technology Transfer Mode'. *Journal of International Business Studies*, Summer.

De la Garza, J.M., and Mitropoulos, P. (1992) 'Technology Transfer of Export Systems at Stone & Webster Engineering Corporation: A Case Study'. *Building Research and Information*, 20 (4), pp.236-241.

Ding, C. (1998) 'Market Opening: China's Construction Industry Has to Be Faced With'. *Construction Economy*, No. 3, p.3.

Du, J. (1997) 'Formation and Development of Large-sized Back-bone, Construction Enterprises 'Difficulties and Opportunities for the Back-bone'. *Construction Economy*, No. 5, pp.11

Du, J. (1997) 'Construction Enterprises under the Circumstances of Changing Mechanism'. *Construction Economy*, No. 5, pp.11.

Du, X., and Li, X. (1997) 'Attention to the Researches of Management Strategy in Construction Enterprises'. *Construction Economy*, No. 1, p.12.

Fu, Y.C. (1996) 'On Some Principal Matters of International Engineering Contracts'. *Construction Economy*, No. 7, p.21.

Glass, A.J., and Saggi, K. (1999) 'Multinational Firms and Technology Transfer' . *The World Bank Development Research Group*, Policy Working Paper 2067.

Godkin, L. (1988) 'Problems and Practicalities of technology transfer: a survey of the literature'. *International Journal of Technology Management*, Vol.3 No. 5.

Hendryx, S.R. (1986) 'Implementation of a Technology Transfer Joint Venture in the People's Republic of China: A Management Perspective'. *Columbia Journal of World Business*, Spring pp.57-66.

Hofstede, G., and Bond, M.H. (1988) 'The Confucius Connection: From Cultural Roots to Economic Growth'. *Organisational Dynamics,* Spring: 5-21.

Holland, D. (1999) 'Ten Ways to Embed Knowledge Management into Organisational Culture'. *Knowledge Management Review*. Issue: 7.

Huang, M.Y. (1998) 'Operational Tactics for International Construction Contracting'. *Construction Economy*, No. 6, pp.46.

International Office, Construction Ministry P.R.C. (1998) 'Current Situation of Management and Operations in Sino-Foreign Joint Venture Construction'. *Construction Economy*, No. 1, p.26.

Jepson, W.B. (1987) 'Technology Transfer and Construction'. *Journal of Construction Management and Technology*, pp.59-65.

Jin, M. (1998) 'Springing up and Development of China's International Contractors'. *Construction Economy*, No. 3, pp.12.

Kainen, A.S. (1993) 'Technology Transfer to Developing Countries Energy World'. No. 213. November.

Karatsu, H. (1990) 'Right Technology: Transferring Technology That is Needed'. *Intersect*, Oct., pp.10-13.

Kedia, B.L., and Bhagat, R.S. (1988) 'Cultural Constraints on Transfer of Technology across Nations: Implications for Research in International and Comparative Management'. *Academy of Management Review*, 13(4), pp. 559-571.

Kogut, B., and Zander, U. (1992) 'Knowledge of the Firm, Combinative Capabilities, and the Replication of Technology'. *Organisation Science*, 3, 3.

Koizumi, T. (1982) 'Absorption and Adaptation: Japanese Inventiveness In Technological Development' in Lundstedt, S.B. and Colglazier, E.W. Jr. (eds) *Managing innovation: The Social Dimensions of Creativity, Invention and Technology* New York: Pergamon, pp.190-206.

Kumaraswamy, M.M. (1998) 'Industry Development through Creative Project Packaging and integrated Management. Engineering', *Construction and Architectural Management*, 5/3, pp. 228-237.

Lam, A. (1997) 'Embeded Firms, Embeded Knowledge: Problems of Collaboration and Knowledge Transfer in Global Co-operative Ventures'. *Organisation Studies*.

Li, Y.S., and Song, W.G. (1998) 'Competitive Tendering Practice in Chinese Construction'. *Journal of Construction Engineering and Management*, pp. 155-161.

Lu, Y.J., and Zhang, Q. (1997) 'Building Economics Research in the People's Republic of China: A Review'. *Construction Management and Economics* Volume 15, No.5.

Li, Z.Y., Wang, Z.X., and Rui, Z. (1997) 'Thinking about the Development of China's Construction Industry'. *Construction Economy*, No.8, pp. 2.

Maitland, A. (1999) 'Management Knowledge Management: Lessons can be learned from failed attempts to capture and use employees' knowledge'. *Management and Technology. The Financial Times*.

McAulay, L., Russell, G., and Sims, J. (1997) 'Tacit Knowledge for Competitive Advantage'. *Management Accounting (British)*, Volume 75, No.11.

Menzler-Hokkanen, I. (1995) 'Multinational Enterprises and Technology Transfer'. *International Journal of Technology Management*, 10 2/3, p.295.

Miller, R. (1997) 'International Joint Venture in Developing Countries'. *Finance & Development*.

Mustapha, F. (1997) 'Factors Influencing the Effectiveness of Construction Site Managers'. *International Journal of Project Management*, Vol.16, No. 1. Elsevier Science Ltd and IPMA.

Ofori, G. (1994) 'Construction Industry Development: Role of Technology Transfer'. *Construction Management and Economics* 12(5) ,pp.379-392.

Oldham, G. (1987) 'The Transfer of Technologies to Developing Countries'. *Appropriate Technology*, Volume 14-3, pp.12-13.

Proverbs, D.G., Olomolaiye, P.O., and Harris, F.C. (1987) 'Planned Construction Times and Labor Utilization - A Comparison of UK and French Contractors'. *Engineering, Construction and Architectural Management*, 3/3, pp.219-232.

Ramaer, J. (1967) 'Know how and its Transfer - Do we know how'. *Industrial Research and Development News* Volume.

Raftery, J. (1998) 'From Ptolemy to Heisenbery: Quantitative Models and Reality'. *Construction Management and Economics*, 16, pp.295-302.

Research Group on Intensive Operating Of CSCEC (1997) 'Our Train of Thought and Selection of Intensive Operation'. *China State Construction Engineering Corporation Construction Economy*, No. 6, pp.10.

Scott, N., Ponniah, D., and Saud, B. (1997) 'A Window on Management Training within the Construction Industry'. *Industrial and Commercial training*, Volume 29, Issue 5.

Shen, W. (1997) 'Study on Development Styles of Construction Enterprises Groups'. *Construction Economy*, No. 7, p.17.

Sun, J. (1997) 'China's Project Management on the Process of Internationalisation'. *Construction Economy*, No.4, pp. 24.

Sun, Q., and Yao, H. (1998) 'Study on International Project Claims through Looking into the Xiao-Lang-Di Project'. *Construction Economy*, No. 4, pp. 37.

Tian, W. (1997) 'The Application of FIDIC in International Contracting'. *Construction Economy*, No. 9, pp.23.

Thiam, S. T., and Chwee, T. H. (1990) 'Role of Transnational Corporations in Transfer of Technology to Singapore'. *Technology Transfer in the Developing Countries UK Monographs*, pp. 335-344.

Tsang, E.W.K. (1995) 'The Implementation of Technology Transfer in Sino-foreign Joint Ventures'. *International Journal of Technology Management*, 10, 7/8, pp. 757-766.

Tsang, E.W.K. (1997) 'Choice of International Technology Transfer Mode: A Resource-based View'. *Management International Review*, v37 n2 p151 (18).

Tsang, E.W.K. (1998) 'Strategies for Transferring Technology to China'. *Long Range Planning*, Vol.27, No.3, pp.98-107.

Tung, R. L. (1994) 'Human Resource Issues and Technology Transfer'. *The International Journal of Human Resource Management*, V5:4.

Wu, H.J. (1998) 'Outside Orientation of China's Construction Market'. *Construction Economy*, No. 3, pp. 8.

Wang, M.S. (1997) 'Group's Non-Operation in Construction Enterprises'. *Construction Economy*, No. 1, pp. 21.

Woherem, E.E. (1991) 'Expert Systems as a Medium for Knowledge Transfer to Less developed Countries'. *Science and Public Policy*, volume 18, number 5.

Zhang, Y.M. (1997) 'New Thinking about Intensive Operation in Construction Enterprises'. *Construction Economy*, No.7, pp. 24.

Zhao, H. (1998) 'Comparative Study of Large Construction Enterprises in China, America and Japan'. *Construction Economy*, No. 5, p. 3.

Zhou, Q., aand Lu, Y.J. (1998) 'Dominant Industry, Supporting Industry and Building Industry'. *Construction Economy*, No. 1, p.5.

Zou, J.L., and Li, A.G. (1998) 'Merge and Acquisition (Restructuring) of Construction Contractors'. *Construction Economy*, No. 1, pp.30.

Conference Proceedings

Abi-saab, G.M. (1967) *Reference to the Transfer of Technology to Underdeveloped Countries.* Beirut: conference Proceedings, American University of Beirut.

Althuis, P., and Vervuurt, A. (1983) *Technological Movements on a World Scale Transnational Technology Transfer in the 80's: Myths and Realities.* Proceedings of Symposium 8/12/1982 Delft University Press.

Bolin, R.L. (1990) *Technology Transfer and Management in Export Processing Zones.* Barcelona: The flagstaff Institute.

Chen, J.H., and Wills, D. (1994) *China: Economic Growth and Construction Activity Strategic Planning in Construction Companies* A.J. Etkin International Seminar, Technino, Haifa, Israel June 8-9 pp.387-401.

Egbu, C. (2000) *Knowledge Management in Construction SMEs: Coping with the Issues of Structure, Culture, Commitment and Motivation.* Proceedings of the Sixteenth Annual Conference of association of Researcher in Construction Management (ARCOM), Glasgow Caledonian University, September 6-8 2000.

Egbu, C., Sturges, J., and George, C. (2000) *Communication of Knowledge For Innovation within Projects and across Organisational Boundaries.* Proceedings of Congress 200 15th IPMA World Congress on Project Management, Royal Lancaster Hotel, London.

Frappaolo, C., and Tom, W. (1997) *Knowledge Management: From terra Incoggnita to terra firma,* The Delphi group INTNET.

Flanagan, R. (1994) *The Features of the Successful Construction Companies in the International Construction Market,* Strategic Planning Construction. Proceeding of Conference, pp. 304-318 Haifa.

Flanagan, R., and Li, S.R. (1996), *Step by Step Changes in Chinese Construction Companies.* ARCOM Conference Proceedings, pp.388-397.

Garavan, T.N. (1997) *Interpersonal skills training for Quality Service Interaction,* Industrial and Commercial Training, Vol 29, Issues 3, 1997.

Harrold, P., Hwa, E.C.,and Lou, J.W. (1993) *Macroeconomics Management in China.* Conference Proceedings in Dalian, The World Bank Washington, DC

Kumaraswamy M.M. (1994) *Growth Strategies for Less Developed Construction Industries.* ARCOM Conference Proceeding Loughborough.

Li-Hua, R., and Greenwood D. (2000) *Technology Transfer in International Joint Ventures in China,* Glasgow Caledonian University ARCOM Conference Proceedings.

Li, S.R. (1997) *Understanding the Chinese Construction Market.* Reading: ARCOM Conference Proceedings.

Li, S.R. (1997) *How are Chinese Construction Enterprises Meeting the Challenge of Change.* Reading: ARCOM Conference Proceedings

Mansfield N.R. (1986) *Some International Issues from Early 1980's Facing British Consulting Engineers.*ICE Proceedings, 80 (part 1), pp.1211-1231.

Mak, M.Y., Ng, S.T., Chen, S.E. and Varnam, M (2000) *The Relationship between Economic Indicators and Brommilow's Time-cost Model: A Pilot Study* Glasgow Caledonian University ARCOM Conference Proceedings.

Ofori, G. (1992) *Construction Technology Transfer: Issues and Options.* CIB 92, pp.674-477 Conference Proceedings Montreal, Canada.

Yu, Ricky K.T. and Leung Meiyung (2001) *Investigation of Construction Conflict Resolution in Hong Kong,* University of Salford, ARCOM Conference Proceedings.

Reports

Abbott, P.G. (1985) *Technology Transfer in the Construction industry 'Infrastructure and Industrial development' Special Report No. 223 The Economist Intelligence Unit,* The Economist Publications Ltd.

Simmok, E.E. (1989) *Analysis of Factors Impacting Technology Transfer in Construction Projects*. Swedish Council for Building Research.

Stewart, F. (1979) *International Technology Transfer: Issues and Policy Options.* World Bank Staff Working Papers No.344, The World Bank, Washington D.C., USA.

Walsh, M.A. (1987) *Project Management in the People's Republic of China Managing Construction Worldwide.* Ascot: The Chartered Institute of Building.

The World Bank (1981) *Guidelines - Use of Consultants by World Bank Borrowers and by The World Bank as Executing Agency.* Washington, D.C.

The World Bank (1984) *The Construction Industry: Issues and Strategies in Developing Countries.* Washington, D.C., The World Bank, 1997, *China 2020.* Washington, D.C.

Unpublished Papers

Carrillo, P. (1994) *Improving Construction Management Expertise in Developing Countries.* Loughborough University of Technology.

Chen, J. (1994) *Joint-venture in China.* PhD thesis University of Greenwich.

Speech

Stern, N. (2001) Twenty Years of Reform: Achievements, Challenges, and the New Agenda, Tsinghua University, Beijing, PRC.

Newspapers

Economic Daily, 1999, Beijing, PRC.

Zheng J. Y., 1997, *Xiaolangdi Project News*, Xiaolandi Project Management Committee, Zhengzhou, PRC.

Gouna, D., 1997, *China Hydraulic*, Beijing, PRC.

Yearbook

Construction Statistical Yearbook of China, 1998, China Statistical Publishing House Beijing.

Web Site

Http://research.med.umkc.edu/tlwbiostats/corrscat_jmp.html
Copyright 1996 by T. Lee Willoughby.

Index